SAINSBURY'S

COOKING
FOR A HEALTHY
HEART

ANNE HEUGHAN

CONTENTS

Published exclusively for J Sainsbury plc
Stamford House Stamford Street
London SE1 9LL
by Martin Books
Simon & Schuster Consumer Group
Grafton House 64 Maids Causeway
Cambridge CB5 8DD

ISBN 0 85941 838 3

First published 1993

Text, photographs and illustrations
© 1993 J Sainsbury plc

Printed in Italy by Printer Trento

THE AUTHOR

Anne Heughan trained at Sheffield Polytechnic as a Home Economist before going to Manchester Polytechnic to qualify as a State Registered Dietitian. She worked for many years in Newham as a Community Dietitian and was involved in advising the public and other professionals on the benefits of a healthy diet.

As Assistant Director of the Coronary Prevention Group, Anne was responsible for developing campaigns on school meals, secondary prevention and rehabilitation of coronary heart disease, and on nutrition labelling. She has worked for North East Thames Regional Health Authority as the Regional Coordinator on coronary heart disease prevention.

Anne is a judge for the Evian/*Good Housekeeping* Catering Award as she believes much still needs to be done to improve food eaten outside the home. She is a member of the British Dietetic Association, the Royal Society of Medicine Forum on Food and Health and the Faculty of Public Health Medicine Cardiovascular and Smoking Working Group.

Anne lives in rural Essex with her husband.

Pictured on the front cover: Smoked Fish Salad (page 22)
Pictured on the back cover: Hot Pineapple (page 78), Mango Sorbet (page 82) and Apricot Mousse (page 79)

Smoked Fish Salad

Four-Fruit Salad with
Cointreau Sauce

Guinea Fowl with
Couscous

INTRODUCTION

All recipes in this book give ingredients in both metric (g, ml, etc.) and Imperial (oz, pints, etc.) measures. Use either set of quantities, but not both, in any one recipe.

All teaspoons and tablespoons are level, unless otherwise stated. 1 teaspoon = a 5 ml spoon; 1 tablespoon = a 15 ml spoon.

Egg size is medium (size 3), unless otherwise stated.

Vegetables are medium-sized, unless otherwise stated.

Freshly ground black pepper should be used for pepper throughout.

Preparation and cooking times

Preparation and cooking times are included at the head of the recipes as a general guide; preparation times, especially, are approximate and timings are usually rounded to the nearest 5 minutes.

Preparation times include the time taken to prepare ingredients in the list, but not to make any 'basic' recipe, such as a stock.

The cooking times given at the heads of the recipes denote cooking periods when the dish can be left largely unattended,

Many doctors and dietitians now agree about what we should eat to help prevent coronary heart disease. In addition, evidence is emerging that the same diet may also help prevent cancer and protect against maturity onset diabetes. This book explains the latest evidence on healthy eating and provides you with recipes that will make healthy eating tasty and enjoyable.

The UK has one of the highest rates of coronary heart disease in the world. It is hard to predict exactly who is prone to coronary heart disease, but with one in three men and one in four women in the UK suffering from heart disease, we all need to be concerned about it.

Coronary heart disease is related to several 'risk factors', only one of which is diet. Some of these factors are harder to change than others. For instance, you cannot alter your family history, your age, your sex (men are more at risk than women), or your ethnic background (Afro-Caribbean, Asian, Caucasian, etc.), but you can change the other risk factors. The most serious risk to the health of your heart is smoking, followed by high blood cholesterol and raised blood pressure. Blood cholesterol and blood pressure levels are influenced by an unbalanced diet, lack of physical activity, being overweight and stress. The more risk factors you have, the greater your risk of heart disease.

WHAT IS CORONARY HEART DISEASE?

Coronary heart disease often begins with narrowing of the arteries leading to the heart. This narrowing is usually caused by atherosclerosis, a build-up of fatty deposits in the arteries, which restricts the flow of blood to the heart. A heart attack occurs when the supply of blood to part of the heart is completely blocked. A blockage can also be caused by a blood clot, known as coronary *e.g. baking, stewing, and not the total amount of cooking for the recipe. Always read and follow the timings given for the steps of the recipe in the method.*

Calorie and fat content of recipes

At the head of the recipes a note is included of the calorie count for each dish, its total fat content and what part of the total fat is saturated fat.

Chillies

Before cooking, cut the pods in half lengthways and remove the seeds, which are too fiery for most people. Wash the cut-open chilli with cold water. Chillies contain oils that can make your skin tingle and your eyes smart, so always wash your hands well with soap and warm water after handling chillies, and avoid touching eyes, nose or sensitive areas of skin until after you have finished cooking. Those with sensitive skin may prefer to wear thin rubber gloves while preparing chillies.

thrombosis, or a combination of atherosclerosis and a clot.

A blockage can lead to severe damage of the heart or, all too often, to sudden death. Sometimes the narrowing of the coronary arteries causes angina – a severe pain in the chest which can spread to the neck and arms. The pain is caused by a reduced supply of oxygen to the heart and is usually noticeable during exertion or stress. (If you suspect that you may have angina, you should, of course, see a doctor.)

So what causes this narrowing of the arteries? The evidence seems to point largely to our blood cholesterol levels.

WHAT IS CHOLESTEROL?

Blood cholesterol is not harmful. It is a soft, waxy substance that is made in the liver and is carried in the bloodstream. It is required for a variety of body functions, such as the production of hormones and proper cell function.

Usually the body maintains a healthy balance of blood cholesterol – making more if it needs it and getting rid of any excess. Sometimes, however, the balance goes wrong. This is when blood cholesterol and other substances have a tendency to narrow or 'fur-up' the artery walls, so the higher the level of cholesterol in the blood, the greater the risk of developing coronary heart disease.

Raised blood cholesterol is mainly caused by eating too much saturated fat. Saturated fat encourages the body to make more cholesterol than it needs or can get rid of. Raised blood cholesterol can also be caused by an inherited disease called 'familial hypercholesterolaemia'. This condition affects the liver so that the sufferer cannot get rid of excess cholesterol. It is estimated that 1 in 500 people in the UK suffer from this condition. They usually have extremely high levels of blood cholesterol and treatment can involve following a strict diet and taking a course of drugs.

THE BASIC RULES FOR EATING FOR A HEALTHY HEART ARE:

- *eat more foods rich in complex carbohydrates, particularly bread, rice, pasta, fruit and vegetables*
- *eat less fat, particularly saturated fat*
- *reduce the amount of salt and added sugar we eat*
- *maintain ideal body weight*

WHAT TYPE OF DIET WILL HELP PREVENT CORONARY HEART DISEASE?

In recent years there have been numerous newspaper reports claiming that certain foods, such as garlic, oranges and wine, will help prevent heart disease. Sadly, it is unlikely that there are any such 'magical foods'! Our overall diet and lifestyle are far more important.

COMPLEX CARBOHYDRATES

'Simple carbohydrates' is the term used to describe sugars, such as honey, fructose, sucrose and glucose whereas 'complex carbohydrates' is the term used to describe starchy, plant-based foods; we should eat more foods rich in complex carbohydrates, such as fruit and vegetables, cereals (particularly the wholemeal varieties), beans and pulses. Most are low in fat and contain plenty of vitamins, minerals and dietary fibre.

Studies confirm that, where intakes of complex carbohydrates are high and intake of fat is low, there is less risk of coronary heart disease. The exact role of complex carbohydrates is hard to isolate because diets high in complex carbohydrates are usually also low in total fat (in particular saturated fat). It may be that these reduced rates of heart disease are due to the fibre content, the vitamin and mineral content, or a mixture of both. A certain type of fibre (soluble fibre), found in beans and pulses, oats, fruit and green leafy vegetables, may help to reduce blood cholesterol levels.

Apart from being rich sources of complex carbohydrates, foods such as fruit and vegetables are rich in vitamins and minerals, particularly the antioxidant vitamins: vitamin C, vitamin E and beta-carotene. Antioxidant vitamins may help to destroy harmful free radicals – substances that may initiate heart disease by causing damage to artery walls.

Generally speaking here in Britain we need to double our intake of foods rich in complex carbohydrates and, in particular, those that are rich in dietary fibre.

FOODS RICH IN:

SATURATED FAT

Fatty meats (sausages, hamburgers, breast of lamb), high fat dairy foods (cream, butter, hard cheeses), cakes, biscuits, pies, snacks, hard margarine, lard, ghee, coconuts

MONOUNSATURATED FAT

Peanuts, avocados, rapeseed oil, olive oil, most soft margarines

POLYUNSATURATED FAT (OMEGA-6s)

Corn oil, sunflower oil, soya oil, sesame oil, polyunsaturated margarines, walnuts, almonds, brazil nuts

POLYUNSATURATED (OMEGA-3s)

Oily fish such as mackerel, salmon, herring, sardines, kippers

REDUCING FAT AND SATURATED FAT INTAKE

♥ *Use less oil in cooking, particularly if browning meat or onions. Use an unsaturated oil such as olive, sunflower, corn or soya oil. Use a non-stick frying-pan.*

REFINED CARBOHYDRATES

Despite their bad press, refined carbohydrates, such as sugar and sugary foods, have not been linked directly with causing coronary heart disease. However, sugar and sugary foods can increase the risk of becoming overweight, thereby increasing the risk of heart disease. Many of us eat far too much sugar and sugary foods. Sugar contains no vitamins and no minerals in any significant amounts, only calories, and it makes much more sense to get these calories from other foods that contain important vitamins and minerals as well.

FATS

Our current intake of fat and, in particular, saturated fat is far in excess of what is beneficial for our hearts. Experts recommend that we obtain 11 per cent of our energy (i.e. our total calories) from saturated fat and 35 per cent from total fat. Current average figures are 17 per cent and 40 per cent respectively.

Not all fats are the same in relation to their effect on coronary heart disease. Foods contain two types of fat; saturated and unsaturated fat and unsaturated fats can be further divided into monounsaturated and polyunsaturated. It is the foods high in saturated fats that we should reduce because, eaten in excess, they will increase our blood cholesterol levels.

As a general rule, saturated fats are found in animal foods, such as meat and dairy foods. Extra lean, reduced or lower-fat varieties of these foods contain less than the fatty or full-fat varieties. Cakes, biscuits and snacks can also be high in saturated fat as they often contain butter or 'hydrogenated vegetable oils'. Hydrogenation is a process whereby manufacturers add hydrogen to vegetable oils to make margarines and fats for baking. This hardens the original oil and increases its saturated fat content.

Unsaturated fats have a rather different effect on blood cholesterol levels and hence on our risk of heart disease. Neither monounsaturated

- Use low-fat dairy foods such as skimmed or semi-skimmed milk, low-fat yogurt and low-fat cheese. Don't use coffee whiteners as a substitute for milk as they are usually high in saturated fat.

- Choose a poly-unsaturated margarine or a reduced-fat or low-fat spread instead of butter or hard margarine. A polyunsaturated margarine will always be labelled 'high in polyunsaturates'. Choose a reduced-fat mayonnaise and a fat-free salad dressing (or make your own dressing with a small amount of unsaturated oil, such as olive oil or sunflower seed oil).

- Try to eat your bread without any butter or margarine, as they do in other parts of Europe, or spread the fat you use very thinly. Cut the bread thicker.

- Don't add extra butter or other fat to vegetables.

- Use low-fat yogurt or low-fat fromage frais instead of cream or ice cream.

- Choose extra lean cuts of meat, such as beef, pork or lamb, and remember to trim the excess fat from the meat.

nor polyunsaturated fat seems to increase blood cholesterol levels so both can be included in a healthy diet. Some polyunsaturated fats, known as omega-6s, can help to lower blood cholesterol levels. These particular polyunsaturated fats are found in seeds and nuts.

Polyunsaturated fats in fish, called omega-3s, do not lower blood cholesterol levels but they help to make the blood less sticky and so less likely to form clots which could block an artery. On present evidence, experts do not recommend that we should buy fish oil supplements, but that we should eat more oily fish, such as mackerel, herring, salmon and sardines. However, don't forget that although white fish may not contain omega-3s, it is very low in saturated fat and is useful to include as part of our diet.

DIETARY CHOLESTEROL

Dietary cholesterol is not the major culprit in causing heart disease that many people believe. This myth persists because many foods that are high in dietary cholesterol, such as meat products and dairy foods, are also high in saturated fat, thus making it difficult for the researchers to sort out which has the most powerful effect on blood cholesterol levels. Reducing dietary cholesterol has much less effect on blood cholesterol levels than reducing the intake of saturated fat. Even so, it is still unwise to eat large quantities of cholesterol-rich food.

Some people are more sensitive to dietary cholesterol than others. For example people with familial hypercholesterolaemia, or with very high levels of blood cholesterol, are usually advised to eat less dietary cholesterol (as well as less saturated fat). So they should cut down on offal, egg yolks and shellfish, particularly prawns, crab and lobster, as they are higher in dietary cholesterol than mussels, scallops, oysters and clams.

- *Choose chicken and turkey as they are low in fat as long as the skin is removed.*
- *Choose fish (both white and oily) more often.*
- *Use less meat by including beans and vegetables in a casserole, stew or stir-fry.*
- *Eat fewer high-fat snacks, such as cakes, biscuits, chocolate and crisps. If you do need something between meals, then replace your usual snacks with bread, fruit or unbuttered bread-type buns or scones.*
- *Have jacket potatoes (without any extra fat) instead of chips.*
- *Choose reduced-fat versions of foods such as crisps and sausages, but remember, these foods are still high in fat.*
- *Use potato topping (without additional fat or eggs) instead of pastry for savoury dishes. Meat pies, sausage rolls and other savoury pastries contain a lot of fat, both in the meat and the pastry.*
- *Grill, bake, steam or microwave foods whenever possible, but if you need to fry think carefully about the amount and type of oil you use.*

MAINTAINING IDEAL BODY WEIGHT

Maintaining ideal body weight is important, as those who are overweight are twice as likely to be at risk of coronary heart disease. Recent evidence suggests that those who have bigger waist than hip measurements may be more at risk from heart disease. However, if you are thin and lean, don't be too complacent, as you still need to consider what you should eat!

Losing weight is not just about dieting. It should be about re-educating your eating habits and taking more exercise.

Fat is certainly the most calorific of all the foods, providing 9 calories per gram, whereas protein and carbohydrate only provide approximately 4 calories per gram. Alcohol is also high in calories, providing 7 calories per gram. So forget the old adage that bread and potatoes are fattening and start tucking in (but without smothering them with fat).

Exercise does not burn up as many calories as we have been led to believe but it is excellent for your general well-being and helps tone up muscles (including your heart).

SALT

No one is quite sure whether salt consumption is directly linked to heart disease, but eating too much salt can certainly lead to high blood pressure. This, in turn, can cause heart disease and strokes.

We eat far too much salt, approximately 12 grams or just over 2 teaspoons a day, which is far in excess of our bodies' requirements of 4 grams or just less than one teaspoon a day. It is recommended, therefore, that we cut down on our salt consumption. All the salt we need comes from bread, cereals, meat, fish, fruit and vegetables. (Although if you drastically increase the amount of exercise you take, you may need to watch your salt intake to compensate for salt lost in perspiration.)

About three-quarters of our salt intake comes from processed foods. There are certain foods which are very salty and these should be limited

♥ Choose vegetable-based sauces rather than creamy ones with pasta.

♥ Cut down on chips and, if you do cook them, cut them thick and straight and fry in an oil that is high in polyunsaturates. Change the oil frequently.

ONE UNIT OF ALCOHOL

♥ one glass, 125 ml (4 fl oz), of wine (8–9%)

♥ 300 ml (½ pint) ordinary beer, lager or cider

♥ 150 ml (¼ pint) strong beer, lager or cider

♥ one small glass, 80 ml (2¾ fl oz), sherry, port or madeira

♥ one pub measure, 24 ml (⅙ gill)★, of spirits, such as gin or whisky

♥ 2 glasses, 250 ml (8 fl oz), low-alcohol (3%) wine

★Note that a Scottish pub measure of spirits is 1.2 units of alcohol

in the diet; they are ham, bacon, soy sauce, cheese, crisps, salted nuts and smoked fish.

The rest of the salt in our diet is added during cooking or at the table. Reduce your salt intake gradually so that your taste buds adapt to eating less salt. Increasing your intake of herbs and spices will help to compensate for the loss of salt. Salt substitutes do contain some salt and will not help you lose the taste for salt.

ALCOHOL

'A couple of drinks will help prevent a heart attack.' What is the truth behind this type of headline? It is true that many studies have shown that moderate drinkers have a lower risk of coronary heart disease than non-drinkers or heavy drinkers. However, many of these studies did not take account of the fact that the non-drinking group also included those who have abstained from drinking for a variety of reasons, some medical. While there is no conclusive evidence that moderate drinking, no more than two units (see left) a day, is good for the heart, it is also true to say that it isn't harmful.

Large quantities of alcohol can raise blood pressure and increase the risk of a stroke. If you have high blood pressure therefore you would do well to consider reducing your alcohol consumption. Generally alcoholic drinks are low in nutrients but high in calories, so increased consumption of alcohol can also lead to weight problems.

This does not mean you have to be teetotal or, if you already are, that you should take up drinking! But you should stick to the present recommended limits of no more than three units a day for men and no more than two units a day for women, with at least a couple of days a week without alcohol consumption.

SO WHAT DOES THIS ALL MEAN?

Eating for a healthy heart is for everyone and not just for those who have been advised to make changes by their doctor.

HEALTHY BREAKFASTS

- *Wholemeal toast and minimal amount of peanut butter (and no extra margarine or low-fat spread)*
- *Porridge and semi-skimmed milk*
- *Oat and wheat flakes, chopped banana and skimmed milk*
- *Wholewheat biscuits with chopped apple and dried raisins and semi-skimmed milk*
- *Glass of fresh orange juice, Granary® toast with scraping of low-fat spread and small amount of marmalade.*

Consider what foods you buy and how you cook your food as both can make a difference to the nutritional content of the diet. Make the changes gradually because a sudden drastic change may result in slipping back into old habits. You could start by changing the milk you drink or the spread you use on bread, as well as trying a new sandwich or recipe once a week.

Eating for a healthy heart means that meals and snacks should consist of plenty of bread, rice, pasta or potato, with lots of vegetables and fruit and fish or a small portion of meat or dairy produce. So choose boiled rice with stir-fried vegetables and pork or a doorstep sandwich filled with lots of salad and tuna, or pasta with tomato sauce and a sprinkling of parmesan cheese, followed by fruit.

HEART HEALTHY BREAKFASTS

Many people no longer eat a cooked breakfast, in fact the trend is to eat a breakfast that is quick and simple to prepare and consists of fruit juice or fruit, toast, breakfast cereal and tea or coffee. This type of breakfast can be excellent nutritionally speaking. Choose a thick slice of wholemeal toast, spread with just a little jam, honey or marmalade and a very small amount of polyunsaturated margarine or low-fat spread. Use skimmed or semi-skimmed milk. Whatever the options, the uncooked breakfast will usually be much lower in fat and higher in fibre than the traditional cooked breakfast.

A cooked breakfast is still permissable for the occasional weekend treat. If you like cooked breakfasts and want to eat them more regularly, why not choose healthier options such as kippers, baked beans on toast or grilled tomatoes and mushrooms on toast?

PREPARING A PACKED LUNCH

- *Provide rice, pasta or bread as the basis of the lunch. If you are using bread, cut it as thickly as possible.*
- *Add some salad such as tomatoes and lettuce. Or alternatively provide some sticks of celery or carrot instead.*
- *Vary the sandwich filling but choose from lean cooked meat or canned fish or low-fat cheese or hard-boiled egg or cooked beans.*
- *Use the minimal amount of polyunsaturated margarine or low-fat spread (or dressing).*
- *Make sure the packed lunch contains some fresh fruit.*
- *Finally include one treat a day but don't always provide crisps or chocolate. Low-fat fruit yogurt or a piece of homemade fruit cake are an ideal alternative.*

HEALTHY PACKED LUNCHES

- *Wholemeal bread sandwiches filled with grated carrot and grated reduced-fat cheese; piece of malt loaf; banana, fresh orange juice*
- *Cooked wholemeal pasta mixed with diced cucumber, canned tuna*

PACKED LUNCHES

The ideal packed lunch should be quick and easy to prepare and appealing to the person that is going to eat it.

CHOOSING CHEESE

Very few cheeses are really low in fat with the exception of fromage frais, cottage cheese and skimmed milk cheese. However reduced-fat hard cheese is much lower in fat than other cheeses. Edam, Brie and Jarlsberg are somewhat lower in fat than other cheeses. These can make a suitable replacement in meals or dishes that require cheese. Alternatively you could use a small amount of strong flavoured cheese such as mature Cheddar or parmesan cheese instead. But as a rule you should go easy on cheese and only eat it occasionally because of its high fat content.

ADAPTING RECIPES

It is perfectly possible to adapt many of your family's favourite recipes so that they are lower in fat, particularly saturated fat, by using fewer fats and oils and fewer high-fat foods than suggested in the original recipe. In addition this can be achieved by using more beans and pulses or vegetables or fruit. For instance, the Pork with Prunes recipe (page 40) in this book has been adapted by using leaner meat, less oil and no cream or butter.

Or if you are making a dish like Shepherds Pie use more potato topping and less meat. In addition you should use only a small amount of polyunsaturated oil to brown the onions and meat and then add extra vegetables (and possibly beans) to the base.

As a general rule try not to add salt to cooking, unless you are making bread when it is used to control the amount it will rise and, unless you find you can do without it, you may still wish to add a little to french dressing to prevent it tasting 'oily'. You will find that your tastebuds will get used to eating less salt. In fact you may even find that food tastes better!

and canned sweetcorn plus a small amount of salad dressing; homemade courgette and carrot cake; apple; fresh pineapple juice

♥ *Wholemeal bap with a small amount of peanut butter; low-fat strawberry fromage frais; banana; fresh orange juice*

♥ *French bread filled with ham and salad; a small packet of low-fat crisps; pear; coffee*

It is easy to reduce the amount of sugar in fruit-based dishes like crumble, stewed fruit, fruit salads, fruit fools and mousses but it is harder to produce acceptable results for some other puddings or cakes and gateaux. So instead of eating them everyday, keep them for an occasional treat.

Many people believe that eating healthily is all about giving up their Sunday Roast but as long as you eat only lean meat, a small amount of gravy and plenty of boiled potatoes (and only one or two roast potatoes) and boiled or steamed vegetables then it is generally not a problem. This could be followed by a fruit crumble and custard made with less sugar and skimmed milk. It is all a question of balance.

FATS AND OILS

Today there are many different fats and oils available and this can be very confusing. Choose either a polyunsaturated margarine or a low-fat spread. When buying an oil for cooking or making a salad dressing choose either a monounsaturated or a polyunsaturated oil as specified on page 9. Some of the more expensive oils such as walnut and olive oil are delicious for making salad dressings due to their rich flavour.

HEALTHY EATING IS NOT BORING

Food is one of life's great pleasures and it should continue to be so even if we change our eating habits. The recipes I have given here prove over and over again that healthy eating can be every bit as delicious and satisfying as any other sort. It can include food from many different cultures; Italian, Mexican, French, Indian, Chinese, Spanish, Greek or even good traditional British cooking, such as Lancashire hot pot, Fish pie, Pease pudding and gammon. By using a variety of foods, applying the basic rules and using herbs and spices there is no end to the number of dishes you can create.

CONCLUSION

The basic rules for a healthy heart are:

- ♥ don't smoke
- ♥ eat more food rich in complex carbohydrates
- ♥ eat less fat, particularly saturated fat
- ♥ eat less salty (and sugary) food
- ♥ maintain your ideal body weight
- ♥ enjoy plenty of physical activity
- ♥ get your blood pressure checked regularly
- ♥ try to relax and enjoy life

THE CORONARY PREVENTION GROUP

The Coronary Prevention Group (CPG) is the only UK charity dedicated to the prevention of coronary heart disease (CHD). The death rate from CHD in the UK is amongst the highest in the world: over 175,000 people die from CHD every year. It takes many lives prematurely and it causes thousands of people disability and pain for the rest of their lives.

CPG's aim is to prevent death and disability from CHD by promoting measures that inform, and motivate and enable people to adopt healthy lifestyles, and to work with government, health professionals and others to adopt policies to the same end.

If you would like to know more about the work of CPG, send a large stamped, self-addressed envelope to:

The Coronary Prevention Group

Plantation House

31-35 Fenchurch Street

London EC3M 3NN

Telephone 071-626 4844

STARTERS AND SOUPS

SMOKED MACKEREL PÂTÉ

Preparation time: 10 minutes + 30 minutes chilling   Serves 4

Per portion: 160 kcal; 7.3 g Fat; 1.5 g Saturated fat

250 g (8 oz) cooked
smoked mackerel fillets

150 g (5 oz) skimmed milk
soft cheese

juice of 1 lemon

pepper

lemon slices or parsley
sprigs, to garnish

*In Britain we are great fans of smoked fish and this
pâté is a classic. A little adaptation reduces the
amount of saturated fat found in many versions.
Serve with fresh wholemeal bread or toast for a
starter that is both elegant and satisfying or as a
quick, delicious lunch.*

Remove the skin and any bones from the
mackerel. Place the mackerel, cheese and lemon
juice in a blender or food processor. Season
with pepper and blend until smooth.
Alternatively, mash the mackerel, cheese and
lemon juice together with a fork.

Spoon the pâté into four ramekin dishes and
chill in the fridge for about 30 minutes. Serve
garnished with lemon slices or parsley.

CURRIED PARSNIP SOUP

Preparation time: 20 minutes + 30 minutes cooking   Serves 4

Per portion: 155 kcal; 3.9 g Fat; 0.5 g Saturated fat

1 tablespoon
polyunsaturated oil

1 onion, chopped

1 tablespoon mild curry
powder

500 g (1 lb) parsnips,
chopped

900 ml (1½ pints) water

pepper

lemon slices, to serve

*Reducing the fat in your diet does not mean reducing
the flavour. Parsnip soup with a mild curry accent
may seem surprising but it is a simple and classic
combination.*

Heat the oil in a saucepan and fry the onion
over a medium heat for 5–10 minutes or until
translucent. Add the curry powder and cook
for a further 2 minutes. Add the parsnips and
water, season with pepper, cover and cook for
20–25 minutes or until the vegetables are soft.

Leave the soup to cool slightly, then purée in

a blender or food processor until smooth.
Return to the pan and simmer for 5 minutes.
Serve garnished with lemon slices.

MEDITERRANEAN PRAWNS WITH TOMATO AND AVOCADO RELISH

Preparation time: 25 minutes + 10 minutes cooking
+ 1 hour marinating   Serves 4

Per portion: 175 kcal; 9.6 g Fat; 1.4 g Saturated fat

Ingredients	

2 tablespoons olive oil

2 tablespoons lemon juice

2 garlic cloves, crushed

16 large, peeled prawns
(preferably raw), thawed if
frozen

bread, to serve

**For the tomato and
avocado relish:**

1 small onion, chopped
finely

2 tomatoes, de-seeded and
diced

1 avocado

¼ teaspoon hot chilli
powder

1 tablespoon lemon juice

pepper

*This is an ideal dish to start a special meal if you ever
find yourself entertaining guests who are suspicious of
healthy eating: the shapes of the prawns and the
tangy, fresh-tasting relish make it a visual treat as
well as a culinary one.*

Whisk together the oil, lemon juice and garlic.
Add the prawns, stir well and leave to marinate
for at least 1 hour.
    To make the relish, put the onion in a bowl
with the tomatoes. Stone, peel and dice the
avocado and add it to the onion and tomato
with the chilli powder and lemon juice. Season
with pepper and mix well.
    Pre-heat the grill. Thread the prawns on to
kebab skewers and cook for 5 minutes on each
side. Serve with the relish and plenty of bread.

CRABCAKES WITH CUCUMBER RELISH

Preparation time: 35 minutes + 30 minutes chilling
+ 15 minutes cooking   Serves 4

Per portion: 176 kcal; 9.0 g Fat; 1.4 g Saturated fat

*These fishcakes with a Thai flavour take a little
trouble to make but you will be rewarded with light,
appetising cakes, with flecks of red pepper and green*

1 dried chilli (optional)

250 g (8 oz) fresh or canned crabmeat (brown and white)

1 shallot, chopped finely

grated zest of ½ lime

2.5 cm (1-inch) piece of fresh root ginger, grated finely

¼ red pepper, de-seeded and chopped finely

2 teaspoons fish sauce or 1 tablespoon fish stock

2 tablespoons chopped fresh coriander

1 small egg (size 4–5), beaten

125 g (4 oz) fresh wholemeal breadcrumbs

2 tablespoons polyunsaturated oil

For the cucumber relish:

½ cucumber

1 teaspoon white malt vinegar

1 teaspoon sugar

coriander. Although frying is often frowned upon by food and health experts because it increases the amount of fat or oil we eat, it can be used as a method of cooking foods in a healthy diet if it is only used occasionally, and if only the minimum of unsaturated oil (such as sunflower oil) is used. Bear in mind too that this dish should be served on special occasions rather than as an everyday staple.

Crush the chilli, if using, in a pestle and mortar or on a board with the back of a metal spoon. Put it in a bowl with the crabmeat, shallot, lime, ginger, red pepper, fish sauce or stock and coriander. Mix well with enough of the beaten egg to make a soft, but not too wet, mixture, then divide the mixture into four.

Spread the breadcrumbs on a plate and place one quarter of the crabmeat mixture in the middle. Shape the mixture into a fishcake (Fig. 1), then spoon breadcrumbs over it, pressing them on until it is completely coated on all sides (Fig. 2). Place the fishcake on a separate plate. Repeat with the remaining mixture to make four fishcakes. Chill the fishcakes in the refrigerator for 30 minutes.

Meanwhile, to make the relish, grate the cucumber into a colander and put a plate on top. Put a heavy weight on the plate and leave the cucumber to drain for 20 minutes. Mix the cucumber with the vinegar and sugar.

Heat the oil in a non-stick frying-pan and fry the fishcakes over a medium heat for 7 minutes on each side. Drain on kitchen paper, then serve with the cucumber relish.

1   2

Crabcakes with Cucumber Relish

Mediterranean Prawns with Tomato and Avocado Relish

Crostini

CROSTINI

Preparation time: 20 minutes   Serves 4

Per portion: 149 kcal; 5.2 g Fat; 0.6 g Saturated fat

2 teaspoons olive oil

1 garlic clove, crushed

230 g (8 oz) can of chopped tomatoes

8 thick slices of French bread, cut on the diagonal

50 g (2 oz) black olive pâté

This Italian starter could hardly be simpler but the simplicity is deceptive: the flavours are intense and could become addictive. You can, if you wish, make your own olive paté in a food processor. Blend 24 pitted black olives with 75 ml (3 fl oz) of olive oil.

Heat the oil in a non-stick frying-pan, add the garlic and cook for 2 minutes. Add the tomatoes and cook, uncovered, for 10 minutes or until thickened. Leave to cool slightly.

Toast the bread under the grill. Spread the slices with the black olive pâté, then top with the tomato mixture. Return to the grill for 2 minutes before serving.

SMOKED FISH SALAD

Preparation time: 15 minutes   Serves 4

Per portion: 154 kcal; 7.7 g Fat; 2.6 g Saturated fat

125 g (4 oz) cooked smoked mackerel fillets

125 g (4 oz) smoked salmon

1 large ripe pear

2 tablespoons (30 ml) lemon juice

1 lettuce

For the dressing:

1 tablespoon (15 ml) polyunsaturated oil

¼ teaspoon French mustard

½ teaspoon sugar

salt and pepper

The sweetness and the juiciness of the pears in this salad provide a wonderful contrast with the smoked fish. If you can, choose red-skinned pears and make it really colourful.

Flake the mackerel and cut the salmon into strips about 1 cm (½-inch) wide and place in a bowl. Peel the pear and cut it into slices, then toss the slices in the lemon juice.

Drain the pear, keeping back the lemon juice to use in the dressing and add the pear to the fish. Remove any bruised or wilted outside leaves from the lettuce. Wash and shred the lettuce and place in the bowl. Mix together the oil and 2 teaspoons of the lemon juice, mustard, sugar, salt and pepper. Toss the salad with the dressing and serve.

Pictured on pages 4/5 and on the front cover

22

SEAFOOD TAPAS

Preparation time: 20 minutes + 15–20 minutes cooking
+ 1 hour chilling   Serves 4

Per portion: 304 kcal; 12 g Fat; 1.6 g Saturated fat

375 g (12 oz) squid

*300 ml (½ pint) fish stock
or 150 ml (¼ pint) white
wine and 150 ml (¼ pint)
water*

*375 g (12 oz) scallops,
thawed if frozen*

*250 g (8 oz) peeled
prawns, thawed if frozen*

*1 red pepper, de-seeded and
sliced*

*2 carrots, cut into very fine
julienne strips*

2 tablespoons olive oil

1 tablespoon lemon juice

1 garlic clove, crushed

20 capers

*20 pimento-stuffed green
olives*

*3 tablespoons chopped fresh
parsley*

*1 tablespoon chopped fresh
oregano*

pepper

French bread, to serve

*Tapas are snacks served in bars throughout Spain
and they are becoming very popular in this country
too. This makes a wonderful starter with chunks of
crusty bread to mop up the juices and, of course, a
glass of dry sherry!*

Rinse the squid well, then pull the head away
from the body, pulling out the soft innards at
the same time (Fig. 1) and discard. Pull the
semi-transparent quill out of the body pouch
and peel off the reddish membrane (Fig. 2) and
discard. Remove and discard the fins and rinse
out the mucous membrane from inside the
body pouch (Fig. 3). Dry with kitchen paper.

Put the fish stock in a saucepan and bring to
the boil. Add the squid and simmer for 15
minutes. Remove and drain. Add the scallops
to the stock and simmer for 3 minutes. Remove
and drain. Cut the squid into rings and cut the
scallops into quarters.

Place the squid, scallops, prawns, red pepper
and carrots in a bowl. Mix together the oil,
lemon juice and garlic, season with pepper and
pour over the fish and vegetables. Add the
capers, olives, parsley and oregano and mix
well. Chill in the refrigerator for at least an
hour before serving with French bread.

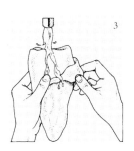

CARROT AND COURGETTE SOUP

Preparation time: 30 minutes + 20-25 minutes cooking   Serves 4

Per portion: 112 kcal; 4.0 g Fat; 0.5 g Saturated fat

25 g (1 oz)
polyunsaturated margarine

1 large onion, chopped

250 g (8 oz) courgettes,
sliced

425 g (14 oz) carrots,
chopped

125 g (4 oz) potato,
chopped

900 ml (1½ pints)
vegetable stock

pepper

I first tried this unusual soup in a pub in Suffolk on a cold winter's day after a long walk. As with most soups it is better and more flavourful with good stock.

Melt the margarine in a saucepan and fry the onion over a medium heat for 5–10 minutes or until the onion is golden and translucent. Add the courgettes, carrots, potato and stock, season with pepper, and cook for 20–25 minutes or until the vegetables are soft.

Leave the soup to cool slightly, then purée in a blender or food processor until smooth. Return to the pan, heat through and serve.

MUSHROOM AND BACON BREAD TARTLETS

Preparation time: 30–35 minutes + 20-25 minutes cooking   Serves 4

Per portion: 123 kcal; 7.7 g Fat; 1.9 g Saturated fat

1 egg

4 teaspoons skimmed milk

1 rasher of back bacon,
de-rinded

25 g (1 oz)
polyunsaturated margarine

75 g (3 oz) mushrooms,
chopped finely

4 slices of wholemeal or
Granary® bread

pepper

Pastry is high in fat but, if you love tarts and pies, there is no need to despair or go without. The new healthy eating is not about self-denial, but about cleverly and gradually adapting your favourite foods. You can wrap flavourful, low-fat savoury (or sweet) fillings in filo pastry or serve this crisp wholemeal bread case with an egg filling as another solution.

Whisk together the egg and milk, and season with pepper. Remove the fat from the bacon, cut the bacon into small pieces and add to the egg mixture.

Heat a third of the margarine in a non-stick frying-pan and cook the mushrooms over a low heat for 10–15 minutes or until soft. Leave to cool slightly.

Preheat the oven to Gas Mark 5/190°C/ 375°F. Roll out the bread with a rolling pin to make it slightly thinner and larger, remove the

*Mushroom and
Bacon Bread Tartlets
Carrot and Courgette Soup*

crusts and spread both sides of the bread with the remaining margarine. Press the bread slices into four 8 cm (3-inch) tartlet tins. You can either leave the four corners of the bread slices to form four 'petals' or you can trim off any excess with a sharp knife.

Add the mushrooms to the egg mixture and pour into the cases. Bake in the oven for 20–25 minutes.

FAKI SOUP

Preparation time: 25 minutes + 40–50 minutes cooking   Serves 4

Per portion: 169 kcal; 4.1 g Fat; 0.5 g Saturated fat

1 tablespoon olive oil

1 onion, chopped

1 garlic clove, crushed

175 g (6 oz) brown or green lentils

227 g (8 oz) can of tomatoes

900 ml (1½ pints) vegetable stock

a pinch of dried mixed herbs

pepper

This is my version of a delicious soup I ate at the house of a Greek friend while I was working in Crete. Even the most dedicated cook needs his or her batch of recipes that are quick and easy to prepare and this definitely falls into that category. This is a fairly thick soup. If you find you need to add a little extra water, then also add 1 tablespoon of tomato purée with each 150 ml (¼ pint) of water.

Heat the oil in a large saucepan and fry the onion for 5–10 minutes or until soft. Add the garlic and cook for a further 2 minutes. Add the lentils, tomatoes, stock and herbs, season with pepper and cook for 35–40 minutes or until the lentils are soft.

Leave the soup to cool slightly, then purée in a blender or food processor until fairly smooth. Return to the pan and reheat for 5–10 minutes before serving.

MEAT AND POULTRY

BEEF FAJITAS WITH PICO DE GALLO

Preparation and cooking time: 35–40 minutes   Serves 4

Per portion: 498 kcal; 13.9 g Fat; 4.7 g Saturated fat

For the pico de gallo:

1 green chilli

2 tomatoes, de-seeded and diced finely

1 small onion, diced finely

1 tablespoon white wine vinegar

1 tablespoon chopped fresh coriander

For the fajitas:

1 tablespoon polyunsaturated oil

1 onion, chopped

1 green pepper, de-seeded and chopped

450 g (15 oz) lean rump steak, sliced very thinly

1 teaspoon ground cumin

1 tablespoon lemon juice

pepper

To serve:

150 g (5 oz) greek-style yogurt

8 chappatis

This chapter provides ample evidence that none of your favourite cuisines need be abandoned simply because you are embarking on a healthier diet. This is a Mexican dish (often served in the USA) – packed with flavour and very satisfying. I have suggested serving the fajitas with chappatis although good alternatives would be nan breads, pitta breads or, most authentic of all, tortillas.

Cut the ends off the chilli, slice it lengthways in half and remove the seeds. Slice the chilli thinly and mix it with the tomatoes, onion, vinegar and coriander. Spoon into a serving bowl.

Pre-heat the oven to Gas Mark 4/180°C/350°F. Wrap the chappatis in foil and heat in the oven for 5–10 minutes or until warmed through.

Meanwhile, to make the fajitas, heat the oil in a wok or large frying-pan and stir-fry the onion and green pepper over a high heat for 5 minutes or until soft but not brown. Add the beef and cook for a further 5 minutes. Add the cumin and lemon juice, season with pepper, stir and cook for a further minute. Turn the fajitas on to a warmed serving dish. You can top your chappati with some of the fajitas, a little pico de gallo and a spoonful of yogurt and then roll it up.

Pork with Water Chestnuts
and Peppers

Beef Fajitas with Pico de Gallo

Lahmacun

LAHMACUN

Preparation time: 30 minutes + 1 hour rising + 25 minutes
cooking   Serves 4

Per portion: 354 kcal; 9.2 g Fat; 1.7 g Saturated fat

*250 g (8 oz) strong white
bread flour*

¼ teaspoon salt

*6 g (¼ oz) sachet of easy-
blend dried yeast*

1 tablespoon olive oil

*about 150 ml (¼ pint)
warm water*

For the topping:

2 teaspoons olive oil

1 onion, chopped finely

1 courgette, chopped finely

*¼ teaspoon hot chilli
powder*

*300 g (10 oz) canned
tomatoes*

1 tablespoon tomato purée

*175 g (6 oz) extra lean
minced beef or lamb*

pepper

*This is my version of a pizza with a delicious spicy
meat topping. I discovered this dish on holiday in
Turkey where you can buy rounds of Lahmacun on
street corners or on the beach.*

Put the flour, salt and yeast in a large bowl and
mix well. Using a wooden spoon, stir in the oil
and enough warm water to make a soft but
manageable dough. (Alternatively put the
flour, salt and yeast in the food processor. Add
the liquid and blend for 2–3 minutes.) Knead
the dough on a floured surface for 10 minutes or
until smooth and elastic. Grease a large
polythene bag with a drop of olive oil, put the
dough inside and leave it to rise in a warm place
for about 30 minutes or until doubled in size.

Meanwhile, to make the topping, heat the oil
in a non-stick frying-pan and fry the onion and
courgette for 5–10 minutes or until soft. Add
the chilli powder and cook for a further minute.
Add the tomatoes and tomato purée, season
with pepper and simmer for 10 minutes or until
thick. Leave to cool, then stir in the meat.

Turn the dough on to a work surface and
knead it for 3–5 minutes, then return it to the
polythene bag and leave it to rise for a further
30 minutes.

Pre-heat the oven to Gas Mark 7/220°C/
425°F. Turn the dough out on to a work surface
again, knock it back and knead it briefly before
dividing it into four. Roll out each piece to a
round measuring about 23 cm (9-inches) across
and no more than 5 mm (¼-inch) thick. Place
the dough rounds on four greased baking sheets
and spread them with the topping. Cover and
leave to rise for 5 minutes, then bake in the
oven for 20–25 minutes or until cooked
through and golden (you will probably need to
do this in two batches). Serve with a salad.

PORK WITH WATER CHESTNUTS AND PEPPERS

Preparation and cooking time: 35 minutes   Serves 4

Per portion: 258 kcal; 12.8 g Fat; 4.0 g Saturated fat

1 tablespoon polyunsaturated oil	There are some regional styles of cooking which are naturally low in fat and Chinese cuisine is definitely one of these. But take care because the Chinese generally like their food salty and the cooking you find in restaurants will reflect this. By all means indulge your taste for Chinese food but be careful with the amount of soy sauce you use – it is very high in salt.

1 tablespoon
polyunsaturated oil

1 onion, chopped finely

1 red pepper, de-seeded and chopped

425 g (14 oz) lean pork tenderloin, cut into 5 cm (2-inch) thin strips

There are some regional styles of cooking which are naturally low in fat and Chinese cuisine is definitely one of these. But take care because the Chinese generally like their food salty and the cooking you find in restaurants will reflect this. By all means indulge your taste for Chinese food but be careful with the amount of soy sauce you use – it is very high in salt.

125 g (4 oz) canned water chestnuts, drained and chopped

1 dried red chilli

1 teaspoon cornflour

1 tablespoon soy sauce

1 tablespoon medium-dry sherry

pepper

Heat the oil in a wok or large non-stick frying-pan, add the onion and red pepper and stir-fry over a high heat for 3 minutes. Add the pork and stir-fry for a further 3 minutes. Add the water chestnuts and whole chilli, and cook for 2 minutes.

Blend the cornflour with the soy sauce, sherry and pepper to taste, and stir it into the pork mixture. Stir-fry for a further 2 minutes. Remove the chilli before serving with rice.

DEVILLED KIDNEYS

Preparation and cooking time: 40–45 minutes   Serves 4

Per portion: 253 kcal; 10.8 g Fat; 2.4 g Saturated fat

8 lambs' kidneys

1 tablespoon
polyunsaturated oil

1 onion, chopped

2 teaspoons mustard powder

2 teaspoons paprika

1/4 teaspoon Cayenne pepper

a pinch of ground ginger

2 teaspoons tomato purée

Devilled kidneys used to be very popular in Victorian times as a way to tempt jaded palates! Kidneys are high in dietary cholesterol, but this is only something to consider if you have a very high blood cholesterol level. On the plus side, however, kidneys are low in fat and high in iron and folic acid.

Cut each kidney in half lengthways and snip out the core with scissors (Fig.). Slice the kidneys thinly. Heat the oil in a non-stick frying-pan, add the kidney and cook over a high heat until browned. Transfer the kidneys to a plate and set aside.

2 teaspoons Worcestershire sauce

2 tablespoons medium-dry sherry

125 ml (4 fl oz) water

pepper

Add the onion to the frying-pan and cook over a medium heat for 5–10 minutes or until golden and translucent. Add the mustard powder, paprika, Cayenne and ginger and cook for 2 minutes. Add the tomato purée, Worcestershire sauce, sherry and water, season with pepper and simmer for 5 minutes. Return the kidneys to the pan and cook for a further 5 minutes. Serve with plenty of brown rice and steamed broccoli.

Cassoulet
Devilled Kidneys

CASSOULET

Preparation time: overnight soaking + 25 minutes + 3 hours cooking   Serves 4

Per portion: 466 kcal; 17.6 g Fat; 6.0 g Saturated fat

125 g (4 oz) dried haricot beans

125 g (4 oz) dried butter beans

4 teaspoons polyunsaturated oil

2 onions, chopped

3 garlic cloves, crushed

175 g (6 oz) lean boneless lamb (e.g. shoulder or leg), trimmed and cut into 2.5 cm (1-inch) cubes

175 g (6 oz) lean boneless pork (e.g. shoulder or leg), trimmed and cut into 2.5 cm (1-inch) cubes

125 g (4 oz) gammon, trimmed and cut into 2.5 cm (1-inch) cubes

This is one of the classic peasant dishes from the South West of France, which combines beans baked with meat. A traditional cassoulet is usually high in fat. However this low-fat version is every bit as good.

Cover the beans with cold water and leave to soak overnight. Drain the beans and place them in a saucepan. Cover with fresh water, bring to the boil and boil rapidly for 10 minutes. Reduce the heat and cook for a further 45 minutes or until the beans are tender. Drain thoroughly.

Heat 2 teaspoons of the oil in a large flameproof casserole, add the onions and fry over a medium heat for 5–10 minutes or until they are golden and translucent. Add the garlic and cook for 2 minutes. Remove from the casserole and set aside. Heat the remaining oil in the casserole, add the meat and cook over a high heat until evenly browned.

Preheat the oven to Gas Mark 3/160°C/325°F. Add the onions to the meat in the pan,

397 g (14 oz) can of chopped tomatoes	add the cooked beans, tomatoes and water, and season with pepper. Tie the bay leaves, thyme and parsley together with cotton or string and add to the casserole. Bring to the boil, then transfer to the oven and cook for 1¼ hours. Reduce the oven temperature to Gas Mark 2/150°C/300°F, cover and cook for a further 30 minutes. Remove the bunch of herbs before serving.
150 ml (¼ pint) water	
2 bay leaves	
2 sprigs of fresh thyme	
4 sprigs of parsley	
pepper	

TURKEY WITH TARRAGON

Preparation time: 10 minutes + 30 minutes cooking   Serves 4

Per portion: 203 kcal; 7.3 g Fat; 2.0 g Saturated fat

4 turkey escalopes	*Turkey escalopes are a very healthy choice and these days not at all expensive. They do however have a tendency to be a little dry. Cooking them this way with wine, orange juice, honey and tarragon not only gives them a lovely fruity flavour, it also ensures they are juicy and succulent.*
20 g (¾ oz) plain flour	
25 g (1 oz) polyunsaturated margarine	
6 tablespoons white wine	
175 ml (6 fl oz) fresh orange juice	Coat the turkey escalopes in the flour. Melt the margarine in a non-stick frying-pan, add the meat and cook over a high heat until browned on both sides. Add the wine and bring to the boil. Add the orange juice, honey and tarragon, season with pepper, cover and simmer over a low heat for 20–30 minutes or until the turkey is cooked.
1 teaspoon clear honey	
4 sprigs of fresh tarragon	
pepper	

SPANISH CHICKEN SALAD

Preparation time: 20 minutes + 30 minutes cooking
+ 30 minutes cooling   Serves 4

Per portion: 297 kcal; 15.6 g Fat; 3.6 g Saturated fat

2 skinless, boneless chicken breasts	*This dish has all the colour and freshness of a salad but is also quite substantial. It is packed with flavour and ideal for a summer lunch.*
2 teaspoons olive oil	
250 g (8 oz) new potatoes	Preheat the oven to Gas Mark 4/180°C/350°F. Put the chicken in a roasting tin with the oil and bake for 25–30 minutes or until cooked.
4 tomatoes	

1 large lettuce, shredded

1 red pepper, de-seeded and cut into strips

20 pimento-stuffed green olives, sliced

4 hard-boiled eggs

For the dressing:

2 tablespoons olive oil

½ teaspoon wine vinegar

½ teaspoon sugar

salt and pepper

Meanwhile, cook the potatoes in boiling water for 15–20 minutes or until tender. Drain the potatoes. Remove the chicken from the oven and leave the chicken and potatoes to cool for 30 minutes.

Cut the tomatoes into six segments each and put in a salad bowl with the lettuce, red pepper and olives. Cut the chicken into large pieces. If the new potatoes are fairly small, leave them whole; if not, cut them into quarters. Remove the shells from the eggs and cut them into quarters. Add the chicken, potatoes and eggs to the salad.

Whisk together the dressing ingredients, pour over the salad, toss and serve.

SPICY CHICKEN

Preparation time: 10 minutes + 1 hour marinating
+ 45 minutes cooking   Serves 4

Per portion: 186 kcal; 6.7 g Fat; 1.5 g Saturated fat

4 part-boned chicken breasts, skinned

For the marinade:

2 teaspoons hot curry powder

2 teaspoons ground ginger

½ teaspoon mustard powder

2 teaspoons ground cumin

4 teaspoons apricot jam

3 teaspoons tomato purée

3 teaspoons Worcestershire sauce

3 teaspoons polyunsaturated oil

4 teaspoons lemon juice

2 garlic cloves, crushed

pepper

At first sight this appears a simple dish but the aromatic marinade imparts a rich golden crusted look to the chicken. Inside the meat will be mouthwateringly tender and spicy.

Cut diagonal slits about 5 mm (¼ inch) deep in the top of the chicken pieces. Mix together the curry powder, ginger, mustard powder, cumin, apricot jam, tomato purée, Worcestershire sauce, oil, lemon juice and garlic in a large bowl. Season with pepper and add the chicken. Make sure it is well covered with the marinade, cover and leave to marinate for at least 1 hour.

Preheat the oven to Gas Mark 5/190°C/ 375°F. Place the chicken in a lightly greased ovenproof dish and cook in the oven for 40–45 minutes, turning halfway through cooking. Serve with nan or pitta bread, brown rice and salad.

Turkey with Tarragon

Spicy Chicken

Spanish Chicken Salad

GUINEA FOWL WITH COUSCOUS

Preparation time: 40 minutes + 1¾–2 hours cooking   Serves 4

Per portion: 481 kcal; 18.4 g Fat; 3.2 g Saturated fat

100 g (3½ oz) couscous

25 g (1 oz) pine kernels

25 g (1 oz) raisins

½ teaspoon ground cinnamon

1 teaspoon ground cumin

4 teaspoons polyunsaturated oil

1 small onion, chopped finely

1.1 kg (2½ lb) guinea fowl

½ teaspoon paprika

6 tablespoons water

For the sauce:

1 teaspoon tomato purée

1 tablespoon lemon juice

1 teaspoon clear honey

¼ teaspoon ground cinnamon

125 ml (4 fl oz) water

The roasting method I have suggested (basting and adding small amounts of liquid) is popular in France and is well worth trying and gives a very succulent result. In France they would use wine but we can cut down calories by using water. The spicy couscous mixture would work well with a chicken but for a really special dinner the guinea fowl is much more unusual and impressive. Couscous is made from the inner part of wheat grain and is a staple food in North Africa.

Put the couscous in a bowl, cover with lukewarm water and leave to soak for 10 minutes. Tip the couscous into a large sieve lined with muslin or a fine-gauge sieve and allow to drain. Place the sieve over a saucepan of boiling water, cover with foil and steam for 35 minutes.

Transfer the couscous to a bowl and add the pine kernels, raisins, cinnamon and cumin. Heat 2 teaspoons oil in a non-stick frying-pan, add the onion and fry over a medium heat for 5 minutes or until soft. Add to the couscous and mix well.

Preheat the oven to Gas Mark 4/180°C/ 350°F. Stuff the guinea fowl with the couscous. (If there is any couscous left over, place it in a greased ovenproof dish, cover with foil and bake for 45 minutes in the oven with the guinea fowl.) Place the guinea fowl in a roasting tin, brush with the remaining oil and sprinkle with the paprika. Bake in the oven for 30 minutes, then baste and add 3 tablespoons of water. Return to the oven and 30 minutes later baste again and add another 3 tablespoons of water. Bake for another 15–30 minutes or until cooked through and golden. Remove from the oven, transfer to a warmed serving plate and leave to rest while making the sauce.

Strain any excess fat out of the roasting tin,

reserving the meat juices. Place the roasting tin over a medium heat, stirring to scrape up and dissolve the sediment left. Pour the juices into a small non-stick saucepan. Add the tomato purée, lemon juice, honey, cinnamon and water, and simmer, uncovered, for 10–15 minutes or until thickened slightly. Serve the guinea fowl accompanied by the sauce.

Pictured on pages 4/5

CHICKEN WITH GINGER

Preparation time: 10 minutes + 1 hour marinating
+ 20 minutes cooking   Serves 4

Per portion: 197 kcal; 6.8 g Fat; 1.7 g Saturated fat

4 skinless, boneless chicken breasts	*Chicken is an established family favourite and this gingery marinade gives it a tangy new twist.*
For the marinade:	
2 garlic cloves, crushed	Mix together the garlic, sherry, ginger, soy sauce, oil and brown sugar. Add the chicken, turn to coat and leave to marinate for at least 1 hour.
1 tablespoon medium dry sherry	
2.5 cm (1-inch) piece of fresh root ginger, grated	Preheat the grill or barbecue. Remove the chicken from the marinade and grill for 8–10 minutes. Turn the chicken pieces, brush with marinade and cook for a further 8–10 minutes or until tender. Serve with brown rice, a rocket or other green salad, and a tomato salad.
3 tablespoons soy sauce	
1 tablespoon sesame oil	
1 teaspoon brown sugar	

ITALIAN CHICKEN

Preparation time: 20 minutes + 50 minutes cooking   Serves 4

Per portion: 236 kcal; 8.9 g Fat; 1.9 g Saturated fat

1 tablespoon olive oil	*In Italy a sauce of tomatoes, onions, garlic, black olives and herbs is one of the staples of good, hearty home cooking. It goes wonderfully well with either chicken or fish.*
4 part-boned chicken breasts, skinned	
2 onions, chopped	
2 garlic cloves, crushed	Heat the oil in a flameproof casserole or large saucepan, add the chicken breasts and fry until evenly browned on both sides. Remove the chicken from the pan and set aside. Add the onions to the pan and fry over a low heat for
397 g (14 oz) can of chopped tomatoes	

125 ml (4 fl oz) dry white wine

50 g (2 oz) pitted black olives

3 tablespoons chopped fresh parsley

pepper

5–10 minutes or until soft. Add the garlic and cook for a further 2 minutes.

Add the tomatoes to the pan with the wine. Season with pepper and simmer for 10 minutes. Return the chicken to the pan, cover and simmer for 20 minutes. Add the olives and parsley, re-cover and cook for another 5–10 minutes or until the chicken is tender. Serve with rice and a salad or seasonal vegetables.

PORK WITH PRUNES

Preparation time: 35 minutes + 25 minutes cooking   Serves 4

Per portion: 323 kcal; 13.2 g Fat; 4.5 g Saturated fat

125 g (4 oz) ready-to-eat dried prunes

200 ml (7 fl oz) red wine

4 boneless pork loin chops, trimmed

20 g (¾ oz) plain flour

20 g (³/₁ oz) polyunsaturated margarine

1 teaspoon redcurrant jelly

pepper

This is another classic French combination with the prunes lending a delicious fruity sweetness and richness to the dish.

Put the prunes in a saucepan with the red wine, cover and cook over a medium heat for 10–15 minutes or until the prunes are soft. Drain the prunes, reserving the wine.

Preheat the oven to Gas Mark 4/180°C/350°F. Coat the pork with the flour. Melt the margarine in a non-stick frying-pan, add the pork and cook over a high heat until browned on both sides. Reduce the heat and continue cooking for about 5 minutes, then transfer the pork to a greased ovenproof dish. Add the prunes, cover with foil and keep warm in the oven.

Add the reserved wine and the redcurrant jelly to the frying-pan and cook for 5 minutes or until slightly thickened. Cover the pork and prunes with the sauce, re-cover with foil and cook in the oven for 20 minutes or until the pork is cooked through.

FISH

FISH PIE

Preparation time: 25 minutes + 1 hour cooking   Serves 4

Per portion: 391 kcal; 6.7 g Fat; 1.6 g Saturated fat

500 g (1 lb) cod steaks
250 g (8 oz) smoked fish
300 ml (½ pint) water
For the sauce:
25 g (1 oz) polyunsaturated margarine
25 g (1 oz) plain flour
300 ml (½ pint) skimmed milk
3 tablespoons chopped fresh parsley
1 tablespoon lemon juice
pepper
For the potato topping:
750 g (1½ lb potatoes)
125 ml (4 fl oz) skimmed milk
pepper

Once you begin to examine your favourite dishes for fat and salt content you may get some pleasant surprises – with just a little alteration they can easily be incorporated in your new healthy diet. For instance smoked fish adds a lovely flavour to this pie but it is very high in salt. Here I have combined it with some white fish. To reduce the fat in this dish still further, you could make a fatless cornflour sauce, with 15 g (½ oz) cornflour and 300 ml (½ pint) of skimmed milk. Blend the cornflour with 2 tablespoons of the milk to form a smooth paste. Boil the rest of the milk in a non-stick pan. Remove from heat and stir the milk into the cornflour paste to form a pouring sauce. If the sauce is not thick enough, clean the pan, add the sauce, return to the heat and stir for 1 minute until thickened.

Preheat the oven to Gas Mark 5/190°C/375°F. Place the fish in a baking dish and add the water. Cover and bake in the oven for 12–15 minutes or until the fish is tender and flakes easily. Remove the fish from the liquid and leave to cool.

Melt the margarine in a non-stick saucepan, add the flour and cook for 2 minutes or until straw-coloured. Gradually add the milk, stirring continuously and bringing the sauce to the boil between each addition of milk. Remove the pan from the heat and add the parsley and lemon juice. Season with pepper.

Remove the skin from the fish and flake the fish with a fork. Mix with the sauce and pour into an ovenproof dish.

To make the topping, cook the potatoes in boiling water for 15–20 minutes or until tender. Drain the potatoes, add the milk, season with pepper and mash. Cover the fish mixture with the potatoes and bake in the oven for 30 minutes or until the topping is browned. Serve immediately with lightly cooked green vegetables, such as beans, broccoli or mange touts, or a mixed green salad.

GRILLED SEA BASS

Preparation time: 5 minutes + 25 minutes cooking   Serves 4

Per portion: 366 kcal; 11.8 g Fat; 4.0 g Saturated fat

1.1 kg (2½ lb) sea bass

juice of 1 lemon

2 tablespoons chopped fresh oregano

pepper

To my mind this is the king of all fish and needs only the simplest of treatments and the simplest of accompaniments. So either serve hot with boiled new potatoes or cold with a green salad.

Clean and de-scale the sea bass, and season with pepper.

Heat the grill to moderately hot. Place the fish in a lightly oiled grill pan and cook for 20–25 minutes, turning halfway through cooking. Transfer the fish to a warmed serving dish. Pour over the lemon juice and sprinkle with oregano. Serve the fish hot with boiled new potatoes and seasonal vegetables, or leave to cool and serve cold with a salad.

FISH IN PAPRIKA

Preparation time: 20 minutes + 25 minutes cooking   Serves 4

Per portion: 181 kcal; 5.5 g Fat; 0.7 g Saturated fat

4 large plaice or lemon sole fillets, skinned, about 175 g (6 oz) each

1 tablespoon polyunsaturated oil

1 large onion, chopped finely

2 teaspoons plain flour

1 tablespoon paprika

Paprika is a wonderful spice – not only does it lend a delicious aromatic sweetness to all kinds of foods but also a lovely golden red colour.

Preheat the oven to Gas Mark 4/180°C/350°F. Roll up the fish fillets, starting with the tail end, and secure with cocktail sticks, if necessary.

Heat the oil in a non-stick frying-pan, add the onion and fry for 5–10 minutes or until golden and translucent. Add the flour and paprika, season with pepper and cook for 2

150 ml (¼ pint) water

pepper

3 tablespoons of low-fat natural yogurt, to serve

minutes. Gradually add the water and bring to the boil, stirring constantly. Then, either place the fillets in a greased ovenproof dish and pour the sauce over them, or pour the sauce into the dish and lay the fillets on the top. Cover and bake in the oven for 20–25 minutes or until the fish is cooked. Remove the cocktail sticks, if necessary, and serve the fish with the yogurt.

SALMON WITH GRAPES

Preparation time: 10 minutes + 20–25 minutes cooking   Serves 4

Per portion: 299 kcal; 17.4 g Fat; 4.3 g Saturated fat

15 g (½ oz) half-fat spread

4 salmon steaks

4 sprigs of dill

125 ml (4 fl oz) white grape juice

pepper

mint and dill, to garnish

For the sauce:

150 g (5 oz) carton of low-fat natural yogurt

2 tablespoons chopped fresh mint

125 g (4 oz) seedless grapes, halved

Once, when all salmon was wild salmon, adding a sauce to this fish seemed almost sacrilegious but the farmed salmon we buy nowadays, though still delicious, can actually benefit from a more adventurous approach. Most of the salmon dishes you see will include cream or mayonnaise – this (much healthier) version is an intriguing (and delicious) blend of flavours.

Preheat the oven to Gas Mark 4/180°C/350°F. Grease an ovenproof dish with the half-fat spread. Place the salmon, dill and grape juice in the prepared dish. Season with pepper, then cover and bake in the oven for 20–25 minutes.

Mix together the yogurt, mint and grapes. Remove the steaks from the dish with a slotted spoon and garnish with mint and dill. Serve with the grape sauce, boiled new potatoes and a selection of seasonal vegetables.

Grilled Sea Bass

Fish in Paprika

BLACKENED SWORDFISH

Preparation time: 10 minutes + 15 minutes cooking   Serves 4

Per portion: 221 kcal; 8.8 g Fat; 1.5 g Saturated fat

3 tablespoons dried oregano

1½ teaspoons black pepper

1½ teaspoons white pepper

1½ teaspoon Cayenne pepper

1½ teaspoons ground cumin

1½ tablespoons paprika

4 thin swordfish steaks

20 g (¾ oz) polyunsaturated margarine, melted

juice of 1 lemon

Blackened swordfish is a Cajun dish which is extremely popular in the United States, but beware – it has a rather dark, spicy taste. However if you like strongly flavoured food, you may like to make up a bigger quantity of the spice mixture and keep some ready in the store cupboard.

Mix together the oregano, black pepper, white pepper, Cayenne pepper, cumin and paprika, and use to coat the swordfish steaks.

Pre-heat the grill to a medium heat. Place the fish on the grill and brush with margarine. Cook under the grill for 7 minutes, then turn and brush with more margarine. Cook for a further 5–7 minutes, then transfer to a warm serving dish, pour over the lemon juice and serve with new potatoes and a green salad, or stir-fried mixed vegetables.

FISH WITH MUSTARD SAUCE

Preparation time: 10 minutes + 20 minutes cooking   Serves 4

Per portion: 204 kcal; 6.3 g Fat; 1.4 g Saturated fat

625 g (1¼ lb) cod fillets, skinned

25 g (1 oz) polyunsaturated margarine

25 g (1 oz) plain flour

3 teaspoons coarse grain mustard

300 ml (½ pint) medium-dry cider

pepper

If you have been trying to find healthier ways of cooking fish instead of frying or adding cheese sauce, this grain mustard and cider sauce may well prove to be the answer.

Preheat the oven to Gas Mark 4/180°C/350°F. Cut the cod into 8 cm (3-inch) strips and place in a greased ovenproof dish. Melt the margarine in a non-stick saucepan and stir in the flour and mustard to make a straw-coloured roux. Season with pepper and cook over a low heat for 2 minutes, stirring constantly. Gradually add the cider, stirring continuously over a medium heat until the sauce comes to the boil and is of a pouring consistency.

Pour the sauce over the fish and cover the dish with foil. Bake in the oven for 15–20 minutes or until the fish is cooked. Serve immediately, accompanied by a mixed pepper salad and fresh crusty bread.

BAKED STUFFED SARDINES

Preparation time: 30 minutes + 35 minutes cooking — Serves 4

Per portion: 383 kcal; 22.1 g Fat; 4.5 g Saturated fat

1 kg (2 lb) sardines (about 16 small sardines)

2 tablespoons lemon juice

2 teaspoons olive oil

lemon wedges, to serve

For the stuffing:

4 tablespoons chopped fresh parsley

75 g (3 oz) fresh breadcrumbs

1 egg, beaten

pepper

The sweetness of fresh sardines is nicely balanced by a lemony dressing and a herby stuffing. This method of layering sardines and herbed crumbs saves the bother of stuffing each fish individually.

Remove the scales from the sardines by scraping the fish from the tail end with the back of a knife, and then cut off the heads and the tails. Cut the fish through the belly and gut them, if necessary. Clean the fish in cold water, then pat dry with kitchen paper. Open the fish out flat, skin-side up, on a work surface, and press down the length of the backbones (Fig. 1). Turn the fish over and remove the backbones (Fig. 2).

For the stuffing mix together the parsley, breadcrumbs, egg and 1 tablespoon water, and season with pepper. Preheat the oven to Gas Mark 6/200°C/400°F. Lay half the sardines flat, skin-side down in a greased ovenproof dish and cover them with three-quarters of the stuffing mixture. Lay the remaining sardines, skin-side up on top of the stuffing.

Sprinkle with the remaining stuffing, the lemon juice and the oil. Bake in the oven for 30–35 minutes or until crisp and tender. Serve with lemon wedges.

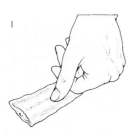

HERRING SALAD

Preparation time: 20 minutes + 1 hour cooking + 1½ hours cooling   Serves 4

Per portion: 309 kcal; 20.8 g Fat; 4.5 g Saturated fat

4 large herrings, cleaned and boned, heads and tails removed

200 ml (7 fl oz) red wine vinegar

1 small onion, sliced

4 cloves

2 bay leaves

6 peppercorns

4 sprigs of dill

For the sauce:

2 teaspoons sugar

2 teaspoons wine vinegar

2 teaspoons French mustard

6 sprigs of fresh dill, chopped finely

4 tablespoons greek-style yogurt

pepper

For the salad:

1 Lollo Rosso lettuce

4 large carrots, grated

½ cucumber, sliced

Today's health experts recommend eating more fish, particularly oily fish such as herring. This unusual salad combines sweet, sharp, piquant and fresh tastes. Use red onions if you can find them – the colours will help make this a very pretty dish.

Preheat the oven to Gas Mark 2/150°C/300°F. Roll each herring, starting from the head end, and secure with a cocktail stick. Place in a deep ovenproof dish and add the vinegar and 4 tablespoons water. Cover with the onion slices, cloves, bay leaves, peppercorns and dill. Cover with foil and bake in the oven for 1 hour. Leave the fish to cool in the liquid for about 1½ hours.

Meanwhile, to make the sauce, mix together the sugar, vinegar, mustard, dill and yogurt. Season with pepper.

Drain the herrings and remove cocktail sticks. Arrange the lettuce, carrot, cucumber, herrings and sauce on four small plates. Serve with wholemeal bread.

Herring Salad
Baked Stuffed Sardines

VEGETARIAN MAIN DISHES

VEGETABLES AND LENTILS AU GRATIN

Preparation time: 35 minutes + 1¼ hours cooking	Serves 4

Per portion: 381 kcal; 15.4 g Fat; 6.2 g Saturated fat

175 g (6 oz) green lentils
250 g (8 oz) broccoli
250 g (8 oz) leeks
250 g (8 oz) cauliflower
40 g (1½ oz) polyunsaturated margarine
40 g (1½ oz) plain flour
½ teaspoon mustard powder
450 ml (¾ pint) skimmed milk
100 g (3½ oz) strong Cheddar cheese, grated
pepper

This has all the virtues of a really good winter supper dish – the sort you really want to come home to on a cold night. I have used full-fat cheeses, rather than reduced-fat, as I prefer the texture and flavour, but I keep the quantity to the minimum so as not to increase the fat content too much.

Put the lentils in a saucepan and cover with cold water. Bring to the boil and boil rapidly, uncovered, for 10 minutes. Reduce the heat, cover and simmer for 15–20 minutes or until soft. Drain and place the lentils in a greased ovenproof dish.

Cut all the fresh vegetables into approximately 4 cm (1½-inch) pieces. Bring a large saucepan of water to the boil, add the vegetables and cook for 8 minutes or until just tender. Drain and place on top of the lentils.

Preheat the oven to Gas Mark 5/190°C/ 375°F. Melt the margarine in a non-stick saucepan and add the flour and mustard powder. Season with pepper and cook for 2 minutes. Remove from the heat and gradually add the milk. Bring slowly to the boil, stirring constantly, until the sauce is smooth and slightly thickened. Add 25 g (1 oz) of the cheese and pour the sauce over the vegetables and lentils. Sprinkle the remaining cheese over the top and bake in the oven for 40 minutes or until the top is golden and bubbling. Serve with fresh crusty bread.

WINTER VEGETABLE STEW

Preparation time: 50 minutes + 1 hour cooking   Serves 4

Per portion: 214 kcal; 6.8 g Fat; 1.3 g Saturated fat

*1 tablespoon
polyunsaturated oil*

2 onions, sliced

*3 carrots, halved
lengthways and cut into
2.5 cm (1-inch) pieces*

*2 parsnips, halved
lengthways and cut into
2.5 cm (1-inch) pieces*

*6 celery sticks, cut into
5 cm (2-inch) pieces*

*2 leeks, cut into 2.5 cm
(1-inch) pieces*

*125 g (4 oz) mushrooms,
quartered*

*375 g (12 oz) potatoes,
scrubbed and cut into 5 cm
(2-inch) pieces*

*½ small swede, cut into
2.5 cm (1-inch) pieces*

4 sage leaves, chopped

2 bay leaves

*6 thinly pared strips of
orange zest*

2 sprigs of fresh thyme

pepper

For the sauce:

*30 g (1¼ oz)
polyunsaturated margarine*

40 g (1½ oz) plain flour

*450 ml (¾ pint) medium
dry cider*

*Warming, heartening dishes, such as this one, often
lean rather heavily on cheese-flavoured sauces and
toppings. This is fine occasionally and in moderation
(see Vegetables and Lentils au Gratin, opposite, and
Aubergine Bake, page 54) but here I have suggested
a tangy sauce made with dry cider – it is unusual,
delicious and it reduces the fat content quite
dramatically.*

Heat the oil in a large flameproof casserole and
add the onions, carrots, parsnips, celery and
leeks. Stir and cook over a low heat for 15–20
minutes or until soft. Remove from the heat
and add the mushrooms, potatoes, swede, sage,
bay leaves, orange zest and thyme. Season with
pepper. Cook over a low heat for about 10
minutes while the sauce is made.

Preheat the oven to Gas Mark 3/160°C/
325°F. Melt the margarine in a non-stick
saucepan, add the flour and cook for 2 minutes.
Remove from the heat and gradually add the
cider. Bring slowly to the boil, stirring
constantly, to form a thin sauce. Pour over the
vegetables and bake in the oven for 1 hour or
until all the vegetables are tender. Remove the
bay leaves. Serve immediately, accompanied by
rice or noodles.

Winter Vegetable Stew

Vegetables and Lentils au gratin

Aubergine Bake

AUBERGINE BAKE

Preparation time: 25 minutes + 30 minutes cooking   Serves 4

Per portion: 152 kcal; 9.0 g Fat; 3.8 g Saturated fat

2 small aubergines, cut into
1 cm (½-inch) slices

1 tablespoon olive oil

1 onion, sliced

2 garlic cloves, crushed

397 g (14 oz) can of
chopped tomatoes

3 tablespoons chopped fresh
basil

100 g (3½ oz)
mozzarella cheese, sliced

pepper

*Recipes often recommend salting aubergines to
remove their bitter juices before including them in a
dish. Personally, I find it makes little difference to
the end result but, if you wish, place the aubergines
in a colander, sprinkle them with salt and place a
plate with a weight on it on top. Leave for 30
minutes, then rinse the aubergines and pat them dry.*

Bring a large saucepan of water to the boil, add
the aubergine slices and simmer for 5 minutes.
Drain and pat them dry with a clean tea towel
or kitchen paper. Place the aubergine slices in a
greased ovenproof dish.

Preheat the oven to Gas Mark 4/180°C/
350°F. Heat the oil in a non-stick frying-pan,
add the onion and fry over a low heat for 5–10
minutes or until soft. Add the garlic and cook
for 2 minutes. Add the tomatoes and simmer
for 5 minutes or until the mixture has thickened
slightly. Add the basil and season with pepper,
then pour over the aubergine. Scatter the slices
of mozzarella over the top and bake in the oven
for 30 minutes or until the cheese is golden and
bubbling. Serve with a green salad and fresh
wholemeal bread.

BEAN AND PESTO CASSEROLE

Preparation time: overnight soaking + 20 minutes
+ 2 hours cooking   Serves 4

Per portion: 294 kcal; 9.1 g Fat; 1.2 g Saturated fat

250 g (8 oz) dried haricot
beans

1 tablespoon olive oil

2 large onions, chopped

1 bulb of fennel, chopped

*Given to me by a dietitian friend, Maggie, this recipe
has become one of my regular feasts. The more
unusual flavours of fennel and red pesto make it
something really special.*

Cover the beans with cold water and leave to
soak overnight. Drain the beans, rinse them

2 garlic cloves, crushed	
3 carrots, sliced	
397 g (14 oz) can of chopped tomatoes	
3 tablespoons red pesto	
1 tablespoon tomato purée	
1 bay leaf	
pepper	

thoroughly and put them in a saucepan. Cover with plenty of fresh water, bring to the boil and boil rapidly, uncovered, for 10 minutes. Reduce the heat, cover and simmer for 1 hour or until the beans are tender. Drain well.

Preheat the oven to Gas Mark 3/160°C/ 325°F. Heat the oil in a large flameproof casserole, add the onions and fry over a medium heat for 5–10 minutes or until beginning to brown. Add the fennel, garlic and carrots, and cook for a further 2–3 minutes. Add the tomatoes, beans, pesto, tomato purée and bay leaf. Season with pepper and stir, then cover and bake in the oven for 1 hour. Serve with salad and fresh crusty bread.

STUFFED PEPPERS

Preparation time: 15 minutes + 1 hour cooking   **Serves 4**

Per portion: 425 kcal; 23.5 g Fat; 6.7 g Saturated fat

4 large green peppers	
75 g (3 oz) long-grain white rice	
125 g (4 oz) frozen sweetcorn	
220 g (7 oz) can of red kidney beans, drained and rinsed	
75 g (3 oz) walnut pieces	
4 tablespoons chopped fresh parsley	
2 fresh green chillies	
550 g (1 lb 2 oz) jar of passata	
100 g (3½ oz) Cheddar cheese, grated	
pepper	

This is one of the classic vegetarian dishes with a stuffing full of different flavours and textures.

Cut the stalk ends off the peppers and remove the seeds. Bring a large saucepan of water to the boil, add the peppers, cover and simmer for 5 minutes. Remove the peppers from the water with a slotted spoon and leave to cool.

Add the rice to the boiling water and cook for 8 minutes. Add the sweetcorn and simmer for a further 5 minutes, then drain.

Preheat the oven to Gas Mark 4/180°C/ 350°F. Mix the rice and sweetcorn with the red kidney beans, walnuts and parsley. Season with pepper and use to stuff the green peppers. Stand the peppers in a greased ovenproof dish. (If there is any leftover rice mixture, place it in the bottom of the dish.) Add the whole chillies. Pour the passata over the peppers and sprinkle with the cheese. Cover and bake in the oven for 1 hour. Remove the chillies, if preferred, before serving the peppers, accompanied by a green salad.

POTATOES IN A SPICY SAUCE WITH CHEESE

Preparation time: 30 minutes + 1¼ hours cooking   Serves 4

Per portion: 293 kcal; 9.5 g Fat; 3.8 g Saturated fat

750 g (1½ lb) small new
potatoes, scrubbed

1 tablespoon
polyunsaturated oil

1 onion, chopped

2 green peppers, de-seeded
and chopped

1 teaspoon fennel seeds

1 teaspoon cumin seeds

a pinch of dried oregano

627 g (22 oz) canned
chopped tomatoes

100 g (3½ oz) mozarella
cheese, sliced

pepper

*Potatoes have to be among the most adaptable
vegetables – lending themselves to all sorts of
treatments and flavours. This spicy potato dish is
based on food from South America – the home of the
potato.*

Cook the potatoes in boiling water for 10–15
minutes or until tender. Drain and place in a
greased ovenproof dish.

Heat the oil in a large saucepan, add the
onion and green peppers, and cook over a
moderate heat for 10 minutes, stirring
occasionally. Add the fennel, cumin and
oregano, and cook for a further 2 minutes. Add
the tomatoes, season with pepper and simmer
for 15 minutes or until slightly thickened.
Meanwhile, preheat the oven to Gas Mark
4/180°C/350°F.

Pour the tomato mixture over the potatoes
and bake for 25 minutes. Remove from the
oven and top with the cheese. Bake for a further
15–20 minutes or until golden. Serve with a
plain green vegetable, such as broccoli, or a
mixed salad.

*Leek Mousse
Potatoes in a Spicy
Sauce with Cheese*

LEEK MOUSSE

Preparation time: 30 minutes + 10 minutes cooling + 20–25 minutes
cooking   Serves 4

Per portion: 187 kcal; 11.7 g Fat; 3.1 g Saturated fat

500 g (1 lb) leeks, cut into
2.5 cm (1-inch) slices

25 g (1 oz)
polyunsaturated margarine

25 g (1 oz) plain flour

4 eggs, separated

pepper

*This delectable vegetable is the basis of some of the
most sensational vegetarian dishes. This soufflé-like
dish looks very impressive and, unlike some soufflés,
it is not prone to collapsing. It can also be made with
spinach or broccoli.*

Preheat the oven to Gas Mark 6/200°C/400°F.
Grease a 1.25-litre (2¼-pint) deep ovenproof
dish or four ramekins.

Put the leeks in a steamer, metal colander or sieve over a saucepan of boiling water, cover and steam for 10 minutes or until tender. Leave to cool for about 10 minutes.

Melt the margarine in a saucepan and add the flour. Season with plenty of pepper and cook for 2 minutes. Transfer to a large bowl and leave to cool slightly. Add the leeks and egg yolks and mix well.

Whisk the egg whites until stiff but not dry, then fold them into the leek mixture. Gently spoon the mixture into the prepared dish or ramekins and bake in the oven for 20–25 minutes, or until risen and set (15–20 minutes for ramekins). Serve with a green salad, baked potatoes and crusty French bread.

TOMATO AND COURGETTE CURRY

Preparation time: 25 minutes + 40 minutes cooking   Serves 4

Per portion: 92 kcal; 3.4 g Fat; 0.5 g Saturated fat

1 tablespoon
polyunsaturated oil

3 onions, chopped finely

1 teaspoon mustard seeds

3 green cardamoms

1½ teaspoons cumin seeds

8 medium tomatoes,
skinned, quartered and
de-seeded

4 courgettes, sliced

This recipe was 'inspired' by a glut of tomatoes and courgettes which our garden produced one summer. This particular combination of mustard seeds, cardamoms and cumin seeds can be enjoyed by those who like food that is spicy but not too hot.

Heat the oil in a saucepan, add the onions and fry over a medium heat for 5–10 minutes or until golden and translucent. Add the spices, cover and cook for a further 3 minutes or until the mustard seeds have stopped popping.

Add the tomatoes and courgettes to the pan, stir, cover and cook over a medium heat for 40 minutes or until the mixture is very soft and pulpy, stirring occasionally to prevent sticking. Transfer to a warmed serving bowl and serve accompanied by warmed pitta bread or crusty wholemeal bread.

PASTA AND RICE DISHES

SPAGHETTI WITH TUNA FISH AND CAPERS

Preparation time: 20 minutes + 25 minutes cooking   Serves 4

Per portion: 444 kcal; 6.0 g Fat; 0.7 g Saturated fat

1 tablespoon olive oil

2 garlic cloves, crushed

230 g (8 oz) can of chopped tomatoes

375 g (12 oz) spaghetti

25 g (1 oz) capers, drained

100 ml (3½ fl oz) dry white wine

4 tablespoons chopped fresh parsley

198 g (7 oz) can of tuna, drained and flaked

pepper

Pasta is low in saturated fat, very satisfying and almost universally popular. All you have to watch is that the sauce you add is not only tasty but also healthy. This dish satisfies those requirements and makes an excellent midweek supper.

Heat the oil in a non-stick frying-pan, add the garlic and cook for 2 minutes. Add the tomatoes and cook for 5 minutes.

Meanwhile, bring a large saucepan of water to the boil, add the spaghetti and cook for 10–12 minutes or until *al dente* (tender but still slightly firm to the bite).

Add the capers, white wine, parsley and tuna to the tomatoes. Season with pepper and cook for 5–7 minutes.

Drain the spaghetti, then return it to the saucepan with the tuna sauce. Toss together over a low heat until heated through, then serve immediately.

PASTA WITH RED PEPPER SAUCE

Preparation time: 30 minutes + 20 minutes cooking   Serves 4

Per portion: 446 kcal; 9.4 g Fat; 2.8 g Saturated fat

1 tablespoon olive oil

2 onions, chopped

4 large red peppers, de-seeded and chopped

5 sprigs of fresh thyme

400 ml (14 fl oz) vegetable stock

Parmesan cheese, used in this dish, has a strong flavour but it also has a high fat content – so use it by all means but keep the quantity small.

Heat the oil in a non-stick frying-pan, add the onion and fry over a medium heat for 5–10 minutes or until golden and translucent. Add the peppers and cook for a further 5 minutes.

375 g (12 oz) tagliatelle
verde

pepper

To garnish:

2 tablespoons roughly torn
fresh basil leaves

40 g (1½ oz) parmesan
cheese, cut into slivers

Add the thyme and vegetable stock, season with pepper and simmer for 20 minutes or until the peppers are soft.

Meanwhile, cook the pasta in plenty of boiling water according to the packet instructions or until al dente (tender but still slightly firm to the bite). Meanwhile, remove the thyme from the pepper sauce, put the sauce in a blender or food processor and purée until smooth.

Drain the pasta and tip it into a warmed serving bowl. Pour over the sauce, then serve immediately, garnished with basil and parmesan cheese.

PASTA WITH SUN-DRIED TOMATOES, PRAWNS AND BASIL

Preparation time: 15 minutes + 20 minutes cooking   Serves 4

Per portion: 501 kcal; 9.6 g Fat; 0.3 g Saturated fat

300 g (10 oz) wholewheat
pasta spirals

750 g (1½ lb) tomatoes,
skinned, de-seeded and
chopped roughly

100 g (3½ oz) sun-dried
tomatoes in seasoned oil,
drained and chopped
roughly

250 g (8 oz) peeled
prawns, thawed if frozen

4 tablespoons chopped fresh
basil

pepper

Sun-dried tomatoes are a real revelation when you first try them – the flavour is so intense. Here they are combined with wholewheat pasta, prawns and fresh tomatoes.

Cook the pasta in plenty of boiling water according to the packet instructions or until *al dente* (tender but still slightly firm to the bite). Drain and return to the pan.

Add the fresh tomatoes and sun-dried tomatoes to the pasta, stir well and cook for 5 minutes. Add the prawns and basil, and season with pepper. Stir well and cook for a further 5 minutes before serving in warmed bowls.

*Pasta with Sun-dried Tomatoes, Prawns and Basil
Pasta with Red Pepper Sauce*

SEAFOOD JAMBALAYA

Preparation and cooking time: 45 minutes   Serves 4

Per portion: 526 kcal; 9.2 g Fat; 0.6 g Saturated fat

1 tablespoon
polyunsaturated oil

1 onion, chopped

300 g (10 oz) easy-cook
long-grain white rice

450 ml (¾ pint) water

¼ teaspoon Tabasco sauce

1 green pepper, de-seeded
and sliced

½ red pepper, de-seeded
and sliced

150 g (5 oz) frozen
sweetcorn

250 g (8 oz) squid, cleaned
(page 23) and cut into rings

125 g (4 oz) peeled
prawns, thawed if frozen

4 large shell-on prawns,
thawed if frozen, to garnish

*This colourful Cajun dish would make the perfect
centrepiece for a summer lunch.*

Heat the oil in a large saucepan, add the onion
and fry over a medium heat for 5 minutes or
until soft. Add the rice and cook for 2 minutes.
Add the water and Tabasco, cover, reduce the
heat and simmer for 10 minutes.

Add the peppers to the pan with the
sweetcorn, squid and peeled prawns. Add a
little more water, if necessary, re-cover and
cook for 5 minutes. Transfer to a large warmed
serving dish, garnish with the shell-on prawns
and serve.

COURGETTE RISOTTO

Preparation and cooking time: 45 minutes   Serves 4

Per portion: 457 kcal; 9.5 g Fat; 1.8 g Saturated fat

1 tablespoon olive oil

1 onion, chopped finely

500 g (1 lb) courgettes,
chopped

1 garlic clove, crushed

¼ teaspoon hot chilli
powder (optional)

375 g (12 oz) easy-cook
American long-grain rice or
easy-cook Italian risotto
rice

*Despite its delicious creamy flavour, this dish is made
with less than half the amount of fat usually found in
a risotto – proving that it is indeed possible 'to have
your cake and eat it'.*

Heat the oil in a large saucepan, add the onion
and courgettes, and fry over a medium heat for
5–10 minutes or until soft, stirring occasionally.
Add the garlic and chilli powder, if using, and
cook for a further 2 minutes. Add the rice and
stir for 2 minutes until it is coated with oil. Add
the wine and simmer, uncovered, until all the

100 ml (3½ fl oz) dry white wine	wine has been absorbed, stirring frequently.
Add 100 ml (3½ fl oz) hot stock and continue simmering until it has been absorbed, stirring frequently. Continue adding the stock, simmering until it has been absorbed between each addition, until all the stock has been used and the rice is just tender. The whole process should take 20–25 minutes. Season with pepper, stir in the parsley and parmesan, and serve.
500 ml (18 fl oz) hot vegetable stock	
3 tablespoons chopped fresh parsley	
25 g (1 oz) parmesan cheese, grated	
pepper	

AUBERGINE PILAF

Preparation time: 30 minutes + 45 minutes cooking + 10 minutes standing   Serves 4

Per portion: 301 kcal; 5.5 g Fat; 0.4 g Saturated fat

500 g (1 lb) aubergines, cut into 1 cm (½-inch) slices	*With your new healthy diet you will be basing meals around sources of complex carbohydrates: rice is ideal and this recipe contains much less fat than traditional aubergine pilafs because the aubergines are partly cooked in water. The nutty flavour of brown rice combines perfectly with the aubergines and mint.*
1 tablespoon polyunsaturated oil	
1 large onion, chopped	
250 g (8 oz) easy-cook long-grain brown rice	Bring a large saucepan of water to the boil, add the aubergine slices and simmer for 4 minutes. Drain the aubergines and pat dry with a clean tea towel or kitchen paper.
230 g (8 oz) can of chopped tomatoes	
1 tablespoon chopped fresh mint	Heat the oil in a large saucepan, add the onion and fry over a low heat for 5–10 minutes, or until soft. Add the aubergine, rice, tomatoes, mint and water. Season with pepper and cook for 40–45 minutes or until the rice is tender, stirring at regular intervals. Remove from the heat and leave to stand for 10 minutes before transferring to a warmed dish and serving with a separate bowl of yogurt.
300 ml (½ pint) water	
pepper	
150 g (5 oz) carton of low-fat natural yogurt, to serve	

Courgette Risotto

Seafood Jambalaya

Aubergine Pilaf

SINGAPORE NOODLES

Preparation and cooking time: 1 hour   Serves 4

Per portion: 546 kcal; 15.7 g Fat; 2.9 g Saturated fat

1 tablespoon
polyunsaturated oil

2 boneless pork loin chops,
trimmed

1 onion, chopped

2.5 cm (1-inch) piece of
fresh root ginger, grated

2 garlic cloves, crushed

1 tablespoon curry powder

2 tablespoons medium-dry
sherry

1 teaspoon tomato purée

1 tablespoon soy sauce

250 g (8 oz) bean sprouts

300 g (10 oz) egg noodles

2 spring onions, chopped
finely, to garnish

*Chinese egg noodles are easy to prepare and a good
source of complex carbohydrates. Here they are
served with a little pork and an Eastern-inspired
blend of spices and ingredients.*

Heat the oil in a large non-stick frying-pan, add
the pork and cook over a high heat until
browned on both sides. Reduce the heat to low
and continue cooking the pork for 15 minutes
or until cooked through. Remove from the pan
and leave to cool.

Add the onion and ginger to the frying-pan
and cook for 5 minutes or until the onion is
soft. Add the garlic and curry powder and cook
for a further minute.

Cut the pork into slices about 1 cm (½-inch)
long and 5 mm (¼-inch) thick and add the
slices to the pan with the sherry, tomato purée,
soy sauce and bean sprouts. Cook for 4
minutes.

Meanwhile, bring a large saucepan of water
to the boil, add the noodles and cook according
to the packet instructions. Drain, and add to the
pork mixture and heat through. Turn into a
warmed serving dish, garnish with spring
onions and serve.

VEGETABLES AND SALADS

ITALIAN SALAD

Preparation time: 15 minutes	Serves 4

Per portion: 14 kcal; 0.3 g Fat; 0.1 g Saturated fat

6 celery sticks, sliced

125 g (4 oz) button mushrooms, sliced

1 large red pepper, de-seeded and sliced

6 tablespoons chopped fresh parsley

juice of 1 lemon

pepper

This salad was inspired by my local delicatessen where I used to buy delicious sandwiches made with wholemeal bread, cooked turkey and this salad.

Place the celery, mushrooms, red pepper, parsley and lemon juice in a bowl. Season with pepper, toss together well and serve as an accompaniment to cold meat or poultry.

CHICK-PEAS WITH SPINACH AND CHORIZO

Preparation time: overnight soaking + 20 minutes + 2 hours cooking	Serves 4

Per portion: 306 kcal; 10.4 g Fat; 2.9 g Saturated fat

250 g (8 oz) dried chick-peas

1 tablespoon olive oil

1 onion, chopped

2 garlic cloves, crushed

½ teaspoon paprika

397 g (14 oz) can of chopped tomatoes

75 g (3 oz) chorizo sausage, sliced

a few strands of saffron

375 g (12 oz) spinach

pepper

Beans and pulses generally go very well with all kinds of pork, the rich, savoury taste of one making a wonderful contrast with the creaminess of the other. This is a colourful Spanish variation with spicy chorizo sausages and spinach.

Cover the chick-peas with cold water and leave to soak overnight. Drain and rinse the chick-peas thoroughly and place in a large saucepan. Cover with plenty of fresh water, bring to the boil and boil rapidly, uncovered, for 10 minutes. Reduce the heat, cover and simmer for 1 hour or until the chick-peas are tender. Drain well.

Heat the oil in a large saucepan, add the onion and fry over a medium heat for 5–10 minutes or until golden and translucent. Add the garlic and paprika, and cook for a further 2 minutes. Remove from the heat.

Add the chick-peas to the onion mixture with the tomatoes, chorizo and saffron. Season with pepper and simmer for 20 minutes. Remove and discard the stems from the spinach and tear the leaves into large pieces. Add the spinach and simmer for 25 minutes or until all the vegetables are soft. Transfer to a warmed serving dish and serve with warm crusty bread.

BRUSSELS SPROUTS WITH CHESTNUTS AND BACON

Preparation time: 40 minutes + 30 minutes cooking   Serves 4

Per portion: 202 kcal; 3.9 g Fat; 1.1 g Saturated fat

375 g (12 oz) chestnuts

4 lean Traditional back bacon rashers, de-rinded

750 g (1½ lb) brussels sprouts

Traditionally popular at Christmas time, this is my husband's favourite winter vegetable dish. Chestnuts are time-consuming to prepare so if you can find canned or dried chestnuts, use these instead. This would be lovely served with roast chicken.

Using a small, sharp knife, cut a small cross in the skin of each chestnut. Put the chestnuts in a large saucepan of cold water and bring to the boil, then reduce the heat and simmer for 5 minutes. Remove from the heat and leave to cool slightly. Taking one chestnut out of the water at a time, remove the outer and inner skins. If the inner skins are hard to remove, place the chestnuts back in the pan of hot water. (The chestnut skins are easier to remove while the chestnuts are warm, so reheat if necessary.)

Preheat the grill and cook the bacon for 10 minutes or until crisp. Meanwhile, cook the brussels sprouts and chestnuts in boiling water for 7–8 minutes or until tender. Drain well and put in a warmed serving dish. Drain the bacon on kitchen paper, then cut it into pieces. Sprinkle it over the sprouts and chestnuts just before serving.

Chick-peas with Spinach and Chorizo
Brussels Sprouts with Chestnuts and Bacon

CHINESE LEAF AND ORANGE SALAD

Preparation time: 10–15 minutes   Serves 4

Per portion: 44 kcal; 1.4 g Fat; 0.1 g Saturated fat

2 oranges

200 g (7 oz) chinese leaves, shredded

For the dressing:

1 teaspoon soy sauce

1 teaspoon polyunsaturated oil

1 teaspoon lemon juice

1 cm (1½-inch) piece of fresh root ginger, grated

This is a pretty combination of delicate colours and an intriguing mix of sweet and fresh tastes.

Cut the top and bottom off each orange. Stand the oranges on a board and use a small, sharp knife to cut off all the peel and pith in vertical strips. Trim off any remaining pith and discard. Turn the oranges on their sides and cut them into slices. Cut each slice into quarters and mix with the chinese leaves in a salad bowl.

To make the dressing, whisk together the soy sauce, oil, lemon juice and ginger, and pour over the salad. Toss the salad well before serving.

SUMMER VEGETABLE SALAD

Preparation time: 15 minutes + 10 minutes cooking + 30 minutes cooling   Serves 4

Per portion: 123 kcal; 3.8 g Fat; 0.2 g Saturated fat

1 small cauliflower, cut into florets

200 g (7 oz) thin green beans, halved

2 courgettes, cut into 2.5 cm (1-inch) pieces

250 g (8 oz) baby carrots

200 g (7 oz) baby corn

For the dressing:

2 tablespoons reduced-calorie mayonnaise

1 teaspoon poppy seeds

2 teaspoons balsamic vinegar

pepper

This makes the most of tender, young vegetables, which are tossed in a creamy-tasting dressing that is still low in fat.

Bring a large saucepan of water to the boil, add the vegetables and simmer for 8–10 minutes or until just tender. Drain the vegetables and place in a bowl.

To make the dressing, mix together the mayonnaise, poppy seeds and vinegar. Season with pepper and mix with the warm vegetables, then leave to cool for 30 minutes before serving.

WINTER SALAD

Preparation time: 15 minutes   Serves 4

Per portion: 107 kcal; 8.5 g Fat; 1.2 g Saturated fat

½ red cabbage, shredded
1 small onion, sliced finely
1 green pepper, de-seeded and sliced finely
1 red pepper, de-seeded and sliced finely
1 yellow pepper, de-seeded and sliced finely

For the dressing:

2 tablespoons olive oil
1 teaspoon wine vinegar
½ teaspoon sugar
½ teaspoon french mustard
salt and pepper

This colourful winter salad makes a change from coleslaw. It can be made up to a day in advance, giving the flavours time to develop and blend.

Place the cabbage, onion and peppers in a salad bowl.

To make the dressing, whisk together the oil, vinegar, sugar and mustard. Season with salt and pepper, pour over the salad and toss well.

CRACKED WHEAT SALAD

Preparation time: 15 minutes + 1 hour 20 minutes standing   Serves 4

Per portion: 197 kcal; 4.4 g Fat; 0.5 g Saturated fat

125 g (4 oz) cracked wheat
2 tablespoons lemon juice
1 tablespoon olive oil
2 tomatoes, chopped
75 g (3 oz) ready-to-eat dried apricots, chopped
4 spring onions, chopped finely
4 tablespoons chopped fresh parsley
2 tablespoons chopped fresh mint
pepper

A salad from the Middle East with a sharp, lemony flavour. This is good as a starter or with grilled chicken or fish.

Soak the cracked wheat in plenty of fresh cold water for about 20 minutes. Rinse and drain the cracked wheat, squeezing out any excess water.

Place the cracked wheat in a bowl, add the lemon juice and oil, and season with pepper. Mix well, then leave for about 1 hour or until the cracked wheat has absorbed the dressing. Add the tomatoes, apricots, spring onions, parsley and mint just before serving.

Summer Vegetable Salad

Cracked Wheat Salad

Winter Salad

BRAISED RED CABBAGE

Preparation time: 15 minutes + 1–1½ hours cooking   Serves 6

Per portion: 66 kcal; Trace of fat; 0.g Saturated fat

1 red cabbage, weighing
about 1 kg (2 lb)

2 onions, sliced

2 cooking apples, peeled,
cored and sliced

1 bay leaf

2 tablespoons red wine
vinegar

1 teaspoon brown sugar

pepper

This is by far the easiest way to cook red cabbage: the result is moist, tender and full of flavour. This would be an ideal accompaniment to Pork with Prunes (page 40) with some baked potatoes.

Preheat the oven to Gas Mark 6/200°C/400°F. Remove the core from the cabbage and finely shred the leaves.

Arrange the cabbage, onions and apples in layers in a large ovenproof casserole, seasoning with pepper between each layer. Add the bay leaf and sprinkle over the vinegar, sugar and 2 tablespoons water. Cover tightly and bake in the oven for about 1 hour or until the cabbage is tender. Remove the cover and cook for another 30 minutes or until most of the liquid has evaporated.

POTATO BAKE

Preparation time: 20 minutes + 2½ hours cooking   Serves 4

Per portion: 413 kcal; 13.6 g Fat; 7.9 g Saturated fat

1 kg (2 lb) potatoes,
scrubbed and sliced thinly

3 lean back bacon rashers,
de-rinded and chopped
finely

2 onions, sliced thinly

450 ml (¾ pint) vegetable
stock

100 g (3½ oz) Cheddar
cheese, grated

pepper

This popular dish is usually full of cream and cheese; my adapted version is much lower in fat but every bit as tasty. To reduce the fat content further, omit the bacon.

Preheat the oven to Gas Mark 3/160°C/325°F. Grease a large ovenproof dish.

Arrange the potatoes, bacon and onions in layers in the prepared dish, seasoning each layer with pepper and finishing with a layer of potatoes. Pour over the vegetable stock, cover and bake in the oven for 1¾ hours. Sprinkle with the grated cheese and bake, uncovered, for another 30–40 minutes or until the top is golden and bubbling.

SPINACH AND POTATO ALOO

Preparation and cooking time: 10 minutes
+ 50 minutes cooking   Serves 4

Per portion: 138 kcal; 4.4 g Fat; 0.6 g Saturated fat

750 g (1½ lb) spinach or
375 g (12 oz) frozen
spinach

250 g (8 oz) new potatoes,
scrubbed and halved

1 tablespoon
polyunsaturated oil

1 onion, sliced

1 garlic clove, crushed

1 teaspoon cumin seeds

2 teaspoons mustard seeds

¼ teaspoon hot chilli
powder (optional)

2 tomatoes, skinned and
quartered

*This Indian-inspired vegetable dish is really tasty
and can be served with basmati rice and dhal.*

Remove and discard any tough stems from the
fresh spinach and wash the leaves. Put them in a
large saucepan with just the water clinging to
the leaves, cover and cook over a low heat for
about 15 minutes or until tender. Drain well,
pressing the spinach gently with a potato
masher to squeeze out all excess water.
Roughly chop the spinach.

Cook the potatoes in boiling water for 15–20
minutes or until tender. Drain and leave to
cool.

Heat the oil in a non-stick frying-pan, add
the onion and fry over a medium heat for 5–10
minutes or until golden and translucent. Add
the garlic, cumin, mustard seeds and chilli
powder, if using, cover and cook gently for 2–3
minutes or until the mustard seeds have
stopped popping.

Add the tomatoes and 4 tablespoons water to
the pan, cover and cook for 5 minutes. Add the
spinach and potatoes, re-cover and cook for a
further 10 minutes. Transfer to a warmed
serving dish and serve immediately.

DESSERTS

PLUM CRUMBLE

Preparation time: 15 minutes + 25–30 minutes cooking   Serves 4

Per portion: 203 kcal; 7.3 g Fat; 1.6 g Saturated fat

500 g (1 lb) plums, halved and stoned

low-fat natural yogurt or fromage frais, to serve

For the topping:

125 g (4 oz) wholemeal flour (self-raising or plain)

50 g (2 oz) polyunsaturated margarine

50 g (2 oz) caster sugar

*Plum Crumble
Meringues with Berry Sauce*

Healthy eating does not mean that all your favourite puddings must disappear from your diet. A fruit crumble is fine just as long as you are careful how much topping you make and you watch the fat content of the other components in the meal.

Preheat the oven to Gas Mark 5/190°C/375°F. Place the fruit in a deep ovenproof dish and add 1 tablespoon water.

Put the flour in a mixing bowl, add the margarine and rub it in with your fingertips until the mixture resembles crumbs. Stir in the sugar and sprinkle the crumble mixture over the top of the fruit. Bake in the oven for 25–30 minutes. Serve hot with the yogurt or fromage frais.

MERINGUES WITH BERRY SAUCE

Preparation time: 20 minutes + 2¼ hours cooking   Serves 6

Makes about 24 meringues
Per portion: 268 kcal; 3.6 g Fat; 2.0 g Saturated fat

2 large eggs (size 1–2), separated

125 g (4 oz) caster sugar

greek-style yogurt or virtually fat-free fromage frais, to serve

For the sauce:

125 g (4 oz) redcurrants

250 g (8 oz) raspberries

40 g (1½ oz) granulated sugar

Greek-style yogurt is much higher in fat than low-fat yogurt. Used sparingly, however, it can give a creamy taste to many dishes. The meringues can be made in advance and stored in an airtight container for up to 2 months. If redcurrants and raspberries are not available, any fresh or frozen berries will do.

Place the egg whites in a large, clean, dry bowl and whisk until they form stiff peaks. Gradually whisk in half the sugar, adding 25 g (1 oz) at a time and whisking well between each addition until the mixture is stiff and glossy. Add the rest of the sugar and fold it in lightly using a large metal spoon.

Preheat the oven to Gas Mark ½/130°C/250°F. Line a baking sheet with baking parchment.

Spoon the meringue into a large piping bag fitted with a 1 cm (½-inch) nozzle and pipe about 24 meringues on to the lined baking sheet, making sure there is enough space between the meringues for them to spread. Alternatively, use a teaspoon to spoon the mixture on to the baking sheet.

Bake the meringues on a low shelf in the oven for 1½–2 hours or until the meringues have dried out and are crisp and slightly golden. If the meringues start to brown during cooking, cover them with greaseproof paper. Peel the meringues off the paper and leave to cool on a wire rack.

To make the sauce, place the redcurrants in a saucepan with the raspberries and sugar and 5 tablespoons water. Bring slowly to the boil, then remove from the heat and leave to cool. Place 3 or 4 meringues in an individual serving dish. On one side place a spoonful of the berry sauce and on the other side a spoonful of yogurt or fromage frais.

HOT PINEAPPLE

Preparation time: 15 minutes + 30 minutes cooking   Serves 4

Per portion: 222 kcal; 3.9 g Fat; 0.3 g Saturated fat

1 large pineapple

50 g (2 oz) flaked almonds

grated zest of 2 oranges

6 tablespoons brandy

1 tablespoon clear honey

low-fat natural yogurt or fromage frais, to serve

An impressive, exotic fruit in a brandied, honeyed syrup – yet it is still ideal for those eating a heart-friendly diet.

Using a sharp knife, cut both ends off the pineapple and remove the skin. Cut out each line of 'eyes'. (The lines form gentle spirals around the pineapple.) This is done by making two cuts at an angle, one on either side of the 'eyes', to make a 'V'-shaped groove and so remove the lines of eyes (Fig. 1). The lines of peel which remain between the grooves are cut off (Fig. 2). (Alternatively cut off the skin in thickish, vertical strips.) Then cut the pineapple

lengthways into quarters and cut out the core. Cut the pineapple quarters into pieces.

Preheat the oven to Gas Mark 5/190°C/375°F. Place the pineapple in an ovenproof dish with the flaked almonds and orange zest. Mix together the brandy and honey and pour over the pineapple. Cover and bake in the oven for 25–30 minutes. Serve hot with low-fat natural yogurt or fromage frais.

APRICOT MOUSSE

Preparation time: 30 minutes + 2 hours chilling   Serves 6

Per portion: 136 kcal; 0.5 g Fat; 0.1 g Saturated fat

250 g (8 oz) ready-to-eat dried apricots

175 ml (6 fl oz) water

11 g (0.4 oz) sachet of gelatine

500 g (1 lb) carton of virtually fat-free fromage frais

juice of 1 orange

2 teaspoons lemon juice

orange slices, to decorate

Place the apricots in a saucepan with water and bring to the boil. Reduce the heat and simmer for 10 minutes, then remove from the heat, drain, reserving the cooking liquid, and leave to cool for 10 minutes.

Put 3 tablespoons water in a small heatproof bowl, sprinkle over the gelatine and leave to soak for 5 minutes.

Stand the heatproof bowl over a saucepan of simmering water and heat gently until the gelatine has dissolved, stirring constantly. Remove from the heat and leave to cool for 5 minutes. Put the apricots, their cooking liquid, the fromage frais, orange juice and lemon juice in a blender or food processor and blend until smooth. Pour into a bowl.

Gradually blend the gelatine into the apricot mixture, mix well and pour into a 1.2-litre (2-pint) serving bowl. Chill for 2 hours or until set. Decorate with orange slices before serving.

Apricot Mousse

Mango Sorbet

Hot Pineapple

MANGO SORBET

Preparation time: 25 minutes + freezing   Serves 6

Per portion: 146 kcal; 0.2 g Fat; 0.1 g Saturated fat

2 large, ripe mangoes

125 g (4 oz) caster sugar

150 ml (¼ pint) water

juice of 1 lemon

1 egg white, if required (see method)

Amaretti biscuits, to serve

Unlike some sorbets, this has a good, uniformly soft texture – no unexpected bits of ice. The colour is truly vibrant and it has a lovely refreshing flavour.

Peel the mangoes and slice the fruit away from the stones. Put the fruit in a blender or food processor and blend until smooth. Transfer to a bowl.

Put the sugar and water in a saucepan and heat gently, stirring occasionally, until the sugar has dissolved. Bring to the boil and boil rapidly for 5 minutes or until a sticky syrup forms. (The best way to test this is to take a small amount of the syrup out of the pan with a teaspoon, let it cool slightly, then test it with your finger to see if it feels sticky.) Leave the syrup to cool.

Stir the lemon juice and sugar syrup into the mango purée. Freeze in an ice cream maker for 20 minutes or according to manufacturer's instructions. When the sorbet is ready, transfer it to a freezerpoof container and freeze until required.

Alternatively, place the mixture in a shallow freezerproof container and freeze for 2–3 hours or until it is beginning to freeze around the edges. Whisk the egg white until just stiff. Turn the sorbet mixture into a bowl and beat lightly to break down the ice crystals, then quickly fold in the egg white. Return to the freezerproof container and freeze until firm. Serve with Amaretti biscuits.

FOUR-FRUIT SALAD WITH COINTREAU SAUCE

Preparation time: 25 minutes   Serves 4

Per portion: 135 kcal; 1.5 g Fat; 0.1 g Saturated fat

2 small ogen melons

250 g (8 oz) seedless white grapes, halved

2 bananas, sliced

juice of 2 oranges

For the sauce:

125 g (4 oz) half-creamery light cream cheese

grated zest and juice of 1 orange

2 tablespoons Cointreau or other orange liqueur

15 g (½ oz) caster sugar

Fruit salad may seem like the archetypal 'healthy pudding' but, served with this low-fat creamy sauce, it will make a delicious treat.

Cut the melons into quarters and scoop out the seeds. Remove the skin and cut the melon into large chunks. Place the melon in a glass bowl with the grapes and bananas. Pour over the orange juice and mix well.

To make the sauce, put the cheese in a bowl and gradually beat in the orange juice, orange zest and liqueur. Stir in the sugar and mix well. Serve with the fruit salad.

Pictured on pages 4/5

BAKED STUFFED PEACHES

Preparation time: 15–20 minutes + 25 minutes cooking   Serves 4

Per portion: 149 kcal; 6.7 g Fat; 0.5 g Saturated fat

4 large, ripe peaches

50 g (2 oz) ground almonds

25 g (1 oz) caster sugar

1 egg, beaten lightly

100 ml (3½ fl oz) orange juice

low-fat natural yogurt or fromage frais, to serve

Using a sharp knife, cut a small cross in the bottom of each peach and put them in a bowl. Cover the peaches with boiling water and leave for 4–5 minutes. Lift the peaches out of the water and peel off the skins. Cut the peaches in half and remove the stones.

Preheat the oven to Gas Mark 5/190°C/ 375°F. Place the peach halves, cut-side up, in an ovenproof dish. Mix together the almonds, sugar and egg to form a stiff paste. Using a teaspoon, fill the centre of each peach half with the almond mixture. Pour the orange juice into the bottom of the ovenproof dish and cover with foil.

Bake in the oven for 15 minutes or until the peaches are tender. Remove the cover and cook for a further 10 minutes before serving with low-fat natural yogurt or fromage frais.

CAKES AND BREADS

COFFEE AND CINNAMON DROPS

Preparation time: 15 minutes + 10–15 minutes baking   Makes 22–24

Per biscuit: 67 kcal; 3.0 g Fat; 0.7 g Saturated fat

4 teaspoons instant coffee granules

175 g (6 oz) self-raising flour

75 g (3 oz) polyunsaturated margarine

2 teaspoons ground cinnamon

75 g (3 oz) caster sugar

1 egg, beaten

Coffee and Cinnamon Drops
Date and Ginger Scones

These spicy biscuits are a useful stand-by when you occasionally want to indulge in something sweet that is not too wicked!

Put the coffee in a bowl and add 1 tablespoon boiling water. Stir to dissolve, then leave to cool. Preheat the oven to Gas Mark 5/190°C/375°F. Grease a baking sheet.

Put the flour in a bowl, add the margarine and rub it in with your fingertips until the mixture resembles breadcrumbs. Add the cinnamon and sugar. Mix the egg with the coffee mixture, add it to the flour and stir with a fork to make a stiff yet soft mixture. Arrange heaped teaspoons of the mixture on the prepared baking sheet, leaving a gap of at least 2.5 cm (1 inch) between each one. Bake in the oven for 10–15 minutes or until golden brown underneath. Leave to cool on a wire rack.

DATE AND GINGER SCONES

Preparation time: 15 minutes + 15 minutes baking   Makes 10

Per scone: 136 kcal; 3.7 g Fat; 0.8 g Saturated fat

250 g (8 oz) plain wholemeal flour

1½ teaspoons baking powder

50 g (2 oz) polyunsaturated margarine

25 g (1 oz) dates, chopped

A delicious, healthy treat studded with chopped dates and stem ginger. If you can enjoy them without margarine so much the better, otherwise spread them with just a little polyunsaturated margarine or low-fat spread.

Preheat the oven to Gas Mark 8/230°C/450°F. Lightly grease a baking sheet. Mix together the flour and baking powder, add the margarine and rub it in with your fingertips until the

25 g (1 oz) stem ginger in syrup, drained and chopped

25 g (1 oz) light brown soft sugar

150 ml (¼ pint) skimmed milk

mixture resembles breadcrumbs. Add the dates, ginger and sugar, mix well and make a well in the centre. Add the milk and stir in with a fork to form a fairly soft dough. Turn on to a lightly floured surface and knead very lightly. Roll out to about 2 cm (¾ inch) thick and cut out rounds with a 5 cm (2-inch) cutter. Place the scones on the prepared baking sheet and bake in the oven for 10–12 minutes or until risen and firm. Transfer to a wire rack and leave to cool.

CARROT AND COURGETTE CAKE

Preparation time: 25 minutes + 50 minutes baking   Serves 12

Per slice: 151 kcal; 5.1 g Fat; 1.1 g Saturated fat

250 g (8 oz) self-raising wholemeal flour

1 teaspoon ground cinnamon

1 teaspoon ground mixed spice

grated zest of 1 orange

50 g (2 oz) polyunsaturated margarine

175 g (6 oz) light brown soft sugar

125 g (4 oz) carrot, grated

125 g (4 oz) courgette, grated

15 g (½ oz) pumpkin seeds

50 g (2 oz) raisins

1 egg, beaten

2 tablespoons milk

This is simple to make and the result is a cake with a nice moist texture and a lovely orange flavour. The pumpkin seeds add a bit of crunch.

Preheat the oven to Gas Mark 4/180°C/350°F. Grease a 20 cm (8-inch) square cake tin. Mix together the flour, cinnamon, mixed spice and orange zest. Add the margarine and rub it in with your fingertips until the mixture resembles breadcrumbs. Mix in the sugar, carrot, courgette, pumpkin seeds and raisins, then stir in the egg and milk and mix together well. Turn the mixture into the prepared cake tin, level the surface and bake in the oven for 40–50 minutes or until risen and firm. Cool in the tin for 10 minutes, then turn out and leave to cool completely on a wire rack.

CIABATTA

Preparation time: 30 minutes + 7½ hours rising and 1 hour chilling
+ 15–20 minutes baking   Makes 4 loaves (12 portions)

Per portion: 238 kcal; 3.4 g Fat; 0.4 g Saturated fat

*750 g (1½ lb) strong
white bread flour*

*1¼ teaspoons easy-blend
dried yeast*

*500 ml (18 fl oz) warm
water*

*5 tablespoons skimmed
milk*

1 tablespoon olive oil

2 teaspoons salt

olive oil for greasing

*This Italian bread has recently become very popular
in this country. It is excellent served warm with
soups, casseroles, pasta dishes and salads.*

Mix together 375 g (12 oz) of the flour and ¼
teaspoon yeast in a large bowl. Add 200 ml
(7 fl oz) of the warm water, stirring it in with a
fork to form a soft dough. Knead for 3–4
minutes. Grease the inside of a clean polythene
bag with olive oil, put the dough inside it and
leave to rise at room temperature for 4–6 hours
or until it has tripled in size. Put it in the
refrigerator and chill for 1 hour.

Warm the milk and mix with the remaining
300 ml (½ pint) warm water and the olive oil.
If you are using a food processor, combine the
liquid with the risen dough. Then, in another
bowl, mix together the remaining flour and
yeast, and the salt. Again in a food processor,
mix the additional dry ingredients into the
dough. (If working by hand add both liquid
and remaining dry ingredients to the risen
dough and work everything together, using a
wooden spoon.)

Turn the dough on to a floured surface and
knead for 10 minutes or until smooth and
springy. Place in a greased polythene bag and
leave in a warm place to rise for 1 hour or until
doubled in size.

Turn the dough on to a floured surface and
knead briefly for 1 minute. Divide the dough
into four and shape each piece into a rough
rectangle. Place on floured baking sheets, cover
with a damp cloth and leave in a warm place for
30–45 minutes.

Preheat the oven to Gas Mark 7/220°C/
425°F. Bake the loaves in the oven for 15–20
minutes or until slightly risen and lightly
browned. Leave to cool on a wire rack.

YEASTED FRUIT BUNS

Preparation time: 35 minutes + 1½ hours rising
+ 20 minutes baking   Makes 14

Per portion: 202 kcal; 3.4 g Fat; 0.3 g Saturated fat

*750 g (1½ lb) strong
brown bread flour*

1 teaspoon salt

*15 g (½ oz)
polyunsaturated margarine*

*6 g (¼ oz) sachet of easy-
blend dried yeast or 25 g
(1 oz) fresh yeast*

*450 ml (¾ pint) warm
water*

50 g (2 oz) flaked almonds

50 g (2 oz) caster sugar

*2 teaspoons ground mixed
spice*

75 g (3 oz) raisins

skimmed milk for brushing

*These fruit buns are very filling and have a very
attractive golden colour. Making buns this way
allows you to make bread rolls with one half of the
dough and fruit buns with the other half. If you wish
to do this, halve the quantities of flavourings used
and add to only half the dough.*

Mix together the flour and salt, add the
margarine and rub it in with your fingertips
until the mixture resembles breadcrumbs. If
using easy-blend yeast, add it to the flour.
Alternatively, dissolve the fresh yeast in the
warm water. Add the water (or water and
yeast) to the flour mixture to make a firm but
soft dough. Turn on to a floured surface and
knead for 8–10 minutes or until smooth and
elastic. Place in a large greased polythene bag
and leave in a warm place for 1 hour or until
doubled in size.

Turn the dough on to a floured surface and
gradually knead in the almonds, sugar, mixed
spice and raisins. This will take about 5
minutes. Shape the mixture into 14 rolls and
place on greased baking sheets. Cover with
greased clingfilm and leave to rise in a warm
place for 30 minutes.

Preheat the oven to Gas Mark 7/220°C/
425°F. Brush the rolls with skimmed milk and
bake in the oven for 15–20 minutes or until the
rolls sound hollow when tapped on the bottom.
Leave to cool on a wire rack.

WALNUT BREAD

Preparation time: 30 minutes + 1 hour 40 minutes rising
+ 35 minutes baking

Makes 2 loaves (24 slices)

Per slice: 121 kcal; 2.5 g Fat; 0.2 g Saturated fat

550 g (1 lb 2 oz)
Granary® flour

200 g (7 oz) strong white
bread flour

2 teaspoons salt

15 g (½ oz)
polyunsaturated margarine

6 g (¼ oz) sachet of easy-
blend dried yeast

50 g (2 oz) walnuts,
chopped

about 600 ml (1 pint)
warm water

*A rustic-looking loaf, studded with pieces of walnut
and with a nutty flavour. This would be lovely
served with a vegetarian dish such as Aubergine
Bake (page 54) and a salad.*

Mix together the Granary® flour, strong white
flour and salt. Add the margarine and rub in
with your fingertips until the mixture
resembles breadcrumbs. Add the yeast and
walnuts, then add enough warm water, stirring
it in with a fork, to form a firm but soft dough.
Turn the dough on to a floured surface and
knead for about 10 minutes or until it is smooth
and elastic. Place in a large greased polythene
bag and leave to rise in a warm place for 1 hour
or until doubled in size.

Turn the dough on to a floured surface and
knead for 2–3 minutes. Divide the dough into
two and shape into two round loaves. Place on
two greased baking sheets, cover with oiled
clingfilm and leave to rise in a warm place for
about 40 minutes or until the dough has
doubled in size and is springy to the touch.

Preheat the oven to Gas Mark 7/220°C/
425°F. Uncover the loaves and bake in the oven
for 35 minutes or until they sound hollow when
tapped on the base. Leave to cool on a wire
rack.

SUN-DRIED TOMATO BREAD

Preparation time: 25 minutes + 50 minutes rising
+ 30–40 minutes baking

Makes 2 loaves (20 slices)

Per slice: 138 kcal; 1.3 g Fat; 0.1 g Saturated fat

750 g (1½ lb) strong white bread flour

2 teaspoons salt

6 g (¼ oz) sachet of easy-blend dried yeast

15 g (½ oz) polyunsaturated margarine

about 600 ml (1 pint) warm water

3 teaspoons red pesto sauce

25 g (1 oz) sun-dried tomatoes in seasoned oil, drained

25 g (1 oz) pitted black olives

The tastes of the Mediterranean permeate this bread, making it an ideal accompaniment to pasta. It is made with easy-blend yeast, which eliminates the need for the first rising and is useful if you are short of time to make bread.

Mix together the flour, salt and easy-blend yeast. Add the margarine and rub it in with your fingertips until the mixture resembles breadcrumbs. Add enough water, mixing it in with a fork, to make a firm but soft dough. Turn on to a floured surface and knead until smooth, elastic and no longer sticky.

Divide the dough into two and shape each half into an oval loaf. Place each loaf on a greased baking sheet. Cut a 2.5 cm (1-inch) deep slit down the middle of each loaf and put half the pesto sauce, tomatoes and olives in each slit. Dampen the slits with water and close by pressing the edges together, then cover the loaves with greased clingfilm and leave to rise in a warm place for about 50 minutes or until doubled in size.

Preheat the oven to Gas Mark 7/220°C/ 425°F. Uncover the bread and bake for 35–40 minutes or until well risen and golden. When cooked the loaf should sound hollow when tapped on the base. Cool on a wire rack.

OATMEAL PANCAKES WITH APPLE SAUCE

Preparation time: 15 minutes + 20 minutes cooking

Makes 6–8 pancakes

Per portion: 119 kcal; 4.1 g Fat; 0.7 g Saturated fat

100 g (3½ oz) plain
wholemeal flour

50 g (2 oz) porridge oats

25 g (1 oz) walnuts,
chopped finely

1½ teaspoons baking
powder

¼ teaspoon bicarbonate of
soda

2 teaspoons light brown soft
sugar

15 g (½ oz) raisins,
chopped

¼ teaspoon ground
cinnamon

¼ teaspoon ground mixed
spice

125 ml (4 fl oz) skimmed
milk

100 g (3½ oz) low-fat
natural yogurt

1 egg, beaten

1 teaspoon polyunsaturated
oil

15 g (½ oz)
polyunsaturated margarine

For the apple sauce:

375 g (12 oz) cooking
apples, peeled, cored and
chopped

50 g (2 oz) caster sugar

a pinch of ground cinnamon

These filling pancakes would make an ideal weekend breakfast or brunch dish.

To make the apple sauce, put the apples, sugar and cinnamon in a saucepan. Add 2 tablespoons water and simmer for 10 minutes or until soft. Beat with a wooden spoon and leave to cool slightly.

Mix together the flour, oats, walnuts, baking powder, bicarbonate of soda, sugar, raisins, cinnamon and mixed spice. Make a well in the centre of the mixture and add the milk, yogurt, egg and oil. Mix to form a thick batter. (This mixture can be made the night before, if necessary.)

Melt half the margarine in a non-stick frying-pan and add 2 tablespoons of the batter per pancake. Don't spread the batter out too much; the pancakes should be about 5 mm (¼ inch) thick. You can cook up to 4 pancakes at a time in the frying-pan. Cook the pancakes over a low heat for about 5 minutes or until their undersides are golden brown, then turn them over with a palette knife and cook the other side until golden. Transfer the pancakes to a warmed plate and keep warm. Melt the remaining margarine in the frying-pan and cook a second batch of pancakes in the same way. Serve the pancakes hot with the apple sauce.

Oatmeal Pancakes with
Apple Sauce

Walnut Bread

Sun-dried Tomato Bread

MENUS

The menu suggestions are to help you understand the new way of eating, which centres on plenty of bread, rice, pasta or potatoes with lots of fruit and vegetables and a minimal amount of meat, fish, eggs and cheese.

Although the fat, particularly the saturated fat, has been kept to a minimum throughout the recipes, you still need to consider which foods you put together. For instance, the crabcakes and the guinea fowl would be fine for a dinner party but rather high in fat for everyday eating.

For most of us eating is one of life's pleasures to enjoy. Bon appetit and good health!

(Dishes marked with an asterisk can be found in this book.)

EVERYDAY LUNCHES OR EVENING MEALS
Bean and Pesto Casserole★
Winter Salad★
Wholemeal bread
Fresh fruit

Seafood Jambalaya★
Green salad
Tomato salad
Granary® bread
Mango Sorbet★

Lahmacun★
Mixed salad
Fresh fruit

Roast chicken
Brussels Sprouts with Chestnuts and Bacon★
Jacket potatoes
Carrots
Low-fat fruit yogurt

Carrot and Courgette Soup★
Wholemeal bread
Leek Mousse★
Chinese Leaf and Orange Salad★
Tomato salad

EVENING MEALS OR LUNCH PARTIES
Spicy Chicken★
Tomato and Courgette Curry★
Italian Salad★
Boiled basmati rice
Fresh fruit salad

Turkey with Tarragon★
Jacket potatoes
Green beans
Apricot Mousse★

Pork with Prunes★
Mashed parsnip
Green beans
Boiled potatoes

DINNER PARTY
Crabcakes with Cucumber Relish★
Guinea Fowl with Couscous★
Courgettes
Carrots
Boiled potatoes
Meringues with Berry Sauce★

BARBECUE
Grilled Sea Bass★
Cracked Wheat Salad★
Tomato salad
Italian Salad★
Bread
Hot Pineapple★

INDEX TO RECIPES

Cover design: Green Moore Lowenhoff
Cover illustration: Sally Swabey
Text design: Ken Vail Graphic Design
Photography: Steve Baxter
Styling: Marian Price
Food preparation: Berit Vinegrad
Illustration: John Woodcock
Typesetting: Goodfellow & Egan, Cambridge